THE STORY OF THE

# Grand Celebration

COMMEMORATING 100 YEARS
OF CHIROPRACTIC

# The Story of the Grand Celebration

## Commemorating 100 Years of Chiropractic

Written by C. Randall Heuston
Principal photography by
Charles Allen, Michael Newell, Wanda Simmons
Design and production by WDG Communications

*This publication was produced under the direction
of the Chiropractic Centennial Foundation
William F. Holmberg, D.C., President
Michael J. Hulsebus, D.C., Chairman,
Commemorative Book Committee*

(frontispiece) D.D. Palmer, the founder of the chiropractic profession

WDG Communications Publishing

The Story of the Grand Celebration
*Commemorating 100 Years of Chiropractic*

WDG Communications
3011 Johnson Avenue NW
Cedar Rapids, Iowa 52405

ISBN 0-9651620-0-1

Printed and bound in the United States of America

*Dedicated to Doctors of Chiropractic*
*everywhere, past, present and future,*
*who have helped and will continue to help*
*millions of people to better health.*

# CONTENTS

# F O R E W O R D

As with many of the projects undertaken by the Chiropractic Centennial Foundation, the idea of a commemorative book initiated debate. Although the CCF board decided in favor – indeed the expectation for at least a souvenir booklet goes back to the beginning of the planning process – some in the profession thought the money might be better spent on research or advertising or continuing education speakers or whatever. If this had turned out to be merely a souvenir booklet, they might have been right.

However, as you'll see when you look through this publication, it is more than a vehicle for profession-wide backslapping. I believe it does exactly what the CCF envisioned, namely, capture in words and pictures not only the highlights of the Centennial year but also the significance of those activities, lending perspective and context to this milestone event. Indeed, it was our growing awareness that the Centennial would be not just a party but a coming together of the profession at a critical point in its history that caused us to push forward with this project even when the budget was tight.

We were fortunate to retain the services of C. Randall Heuston, a seasoned and award-winning journalist, who had worked for two decades in various editorial capacities at the *Quad-City Times* in Davenport, the hometown of chiropractic. He has been at Palmer College for the last several years, enriching that institution's publications and events with his writing and production skills. His other Centennial contributions include scripting the "Evening with Ray Charles" program and producing three music videos for that Palmer event so many of you enjoyed. The charge given him by Michael Hulsebus, D.C., chairman of the commemorative book committee, was to produce an objective look at what happened rather than hype or color what went on. This book does that, showing our warts as well as our beauty marks. It all makes for intriguing reading, and this book lives up to its title, *The Story of the Grand Celebration*.

I know you will enjoy this commemorative book, filled as it is with revealing stories and dramatic photographs that rekindle Centennial memories and add understanding about what occurred in public and behind the scenes. So much happened so fast during the Centennial year that a lot remains a blur. This book brings things into focus.

Those of us who worked hard on the Centennial felt drained as activities began to wind down, but, when I look at this book, the juices start to flow again. Yes, our profession accomplished something pretty amazing with the Centennial. The educational program, all the research and history projects, the documentary, the entertainment and tremendous fellowship provoke my favorite Centennial-year word – fantastic! I know you share my hope that the spirit the Centennial generated will continue to buoy this profession we love.

*William F. Holmberg, D.C.*
President
Chiropractic Centennial Foundation

# PREFACE

When Dr. Michael J. Hulsebus and his committee of the Chiropractic Centennial Foundation first approached me about putting together a commemorative book, I knew this was no mere perfunctory marking of an anniversary.

Chiropractic is no ordinary profession. Its unique approach to health care, its flint-faced resistance to bitter persecution, its internal squabbles and the passion exhibited by so many of its members mark this profession as an extraordinary sociological entity. Here was a stubborn, fractious minority, which had grown and prospered against all odds, still under fire 100 years after its birth and at times looking like it could come apart at the seams. Now this upstart bunch was trying to pull itself together for what a few leaders boldly dubbed a Grand Celebration, raising a collective clenched fist in defiance, pride and hope.

As the Centennial year unfolded, as I watched the agony and ecstasy of Dr. William F. Holmberg, Donald M. Petersen, Jr., Rick Flaherty, David A. Chapman-Smith, Esq., Dr. Guy Riekeman and the rest of the Centennial planners, and as I experienced the Centennial events themselves and saw the joy and affirmation of those who attended, I knew my initial impression wasn't melodramatic.

My concern was to do the Centennial and the profession justice. I know this book falls short of that. Time, space and financial constraints meant a lot of subjective picking and choosing. So much had to be left out. For example, highlights of the education sessions are here, but much of value isn't. This book focuses on what were perceived to be the broader issues providing insight into the profession's future. Much practical and technical information about chiropractic technique, imaging, business management and other aspects went begging.

A more serious qualm is the knowledge that people who made significant contributions to the Centennial's success may have been slighted and names may have been misspelled or left out altogether. Photographs were handed in from several sources and may be inadequately credited. I apologize for any and all of that. The immensity and on-the-fly nature of this project, the errors in computer entry of names from various sources, the changes between printed material and the reality – all those were factors. Like the Centennial celebration itself, this book has flaws. I'm proud of it anyway.

Throughout the many hours spent on this project the conviction about its importance never ebbed. The coming together of the chiropractic profession in a Grand Celebration is a story worth telling. And the people who made it happen and all whose lives were enhanced by it deserve a salute however inadequate to the intensity of their experience.

Thanks go to Dr. William Holmberg, Dr. Michael Hulsebus, Don Petersen, Mary McCubbin and others associated with the CCF who gave clear direction and practical help and encouragement to press on. Special thanks go to Charlie Allen, Mike Newell and Wanda Simmons, photographers who proved their professionalism under pressure, and to Duane and Graham Wood of WDG Communications, who did such a fine job of designing the book and getting it produced. I also must thank my wife, Kari-Mette, and my boss at Palmer College, Juan Nodarse, who were patient with me throughout the many months.

*crh*

# Planning Chiropractic's Grand Celebration

*As the 100th anniversary of chiropractic drew near, the profession found itself roiling with assaults from the media, philosophical and political fragmentation and the threat of managed care. Could chiropractic get its act together enough to celebrate its successes? Could a profession-wide celebration even help address the problems? The planners got busy.*

As the 1990s rolled toward the Chiropractic Centennial, the profession found itself sailing on a turbulent sea. Chiropractic had grown dramatically in its century of struggle to more than 50,000 chiropractors, licensed in every state and helping millions worldwide. Yet storm clouds darkened the horizon. Indeed, the profession was under fire from without and threatened by mutinies within.

The Wilk anti-trust suit may have stopped the organized opposition, but spurred on by pending United States health care reform and possible loss of market share, rival health care providers ducked behind the skirts of the mass media to fire their cannons at the chiropractic nemesis.

First, the *Wall Street Journal* warned about chiropractors' marketing to vulnerable children while concerned medical physicians looked on helplessly. Next, the television show *"20/20"* took chiropractic to task for "skeletons in the chiropractic closet," unethical and unscientific practices of fringe practitioners. Later, *The Crusaders* intensified the televised specter of pathetic people crippled by chiropractic care. The *Associated Press* warned of stroke danger from cervical adjustments. *Consumer Reports* took its shot, as did *Woman's Day*, Ann Landers and the tabloids. Ah, the tabloids. *The National Enquirer*, on a cover featuring actress Loni Anderson in a swim suit, screamed: "It's Dangerous, Doctors Say: Marla (Trump) Takes Baby to Chiropractor – to Stop Her Crying!" *The National Examiner: America's Favorite Weekly* got to the point quickly with this headline: "Warning – Chiropractors Can Kill You!"

*"Warning – Chiropractors Can Kill You!"*

Who was throwing the meat for this media feeding frenzy? Perhaps several were, some possibly with honest concerns, but one name in particular kept cropping up, Murray Simon Katz, M.D. He was an authority quoted by *"20/20,"* and a political movement he backed called Orthopractic was touted in *Consumer Reports* as offering a medically controlled and thus safer alternative to chiropractic. Some chiropractors, albeit a tiny and difficult-to-identify minority, were in league with Katz and ready to present themselves as Orthopractors. To some extent at least, the chiropractic profession was beginning to feed on itself, as practitioners scrambled for acceptance in the emerging health care system.

At the other end of the spectrum from Orthopractic, which would have limited chiropractic to a minor adjunct of medicine, were those who felt that adding medical prerogatives, including dispensing pharmaceuticals, would better equip chiropractors for an expanded primary care role. The push for Doctors of Chiropractic Medicine (DCM) increased the perception among some inside and outside the profession that chiropractic was suffering not only a credibility problem but a full-blown identity crisis.

Yes, the straight-vs.-mixer controversy and other professional schizophrenia had stalked chiropractic from its beginning, but this time the context was different. Although federally instituted health care reform rose up only to fade away, *de facto* reform through so-called managed care was sprinkling its alphabet soup of HMOs and PPOs all over the health care landscape. How would chiropractic fit into this new situation with medical physicians as skeptical gatekeepers? Patient visits to chiropractors reportedly were down, and managed care was fingered as the culprit.

Ironically, at the very time chiropractic was finding its niche elsewhere in the world, winning acceptance for clear-cut roles the profession itself helped define, in the country where chiropractic began the profession appeared to be adrift. Early in the Centennial year several leaders met on the topic "Isolation or Integration?" Should they define their profession to make it acceptable to the mainstream, pull in their horns, as it were, not emphasizing that chiropractic helps more than back pain? Or should they tough it out, if necessary relying on cash practices as in the old days? Many applauded the meeting

as coming to grips with the issues dogging the profession. Others saw it as the ship tossing on the waves and nobody able to find a compass.

Of course, the vast majority of chiropractors showed up at their offices and quietly went about helping their patients, seemingly indifferent to the issues batted back and forth in the chiropractic media. Without fanfare many were joining managed care organizations and working together with medical doctors in multidisciplinary settings. Yet the chiropractic leaders were troubled.

Along the way, a favorable breeze began to blow. A major segment of the profession adopted the Mercy Guidelines, a set of practice standards based on scientific evidence for efficacy. Since guidelines

The CCF planners knew that much was at stake

are critical in the managed care environment, the fact chiropractic was perhaps the first health care profession to produce a set opened the door for inclusion in HMOs. However, this breeze had a nasty bite to it. Based on the Mercy Guidelines, insurance companies began refusing to compensate for certain chiropractic procedures. Soon a few chiropractors were launching lawsuits and in a couple of cases even personal attacks against those who had helped draft the Mercy document. More divisiveness.

Pran Manga, Ph.D., and a team of health economists in Canada published a report for the Canadian

*"Others saw it as the ship tossing on the waves and nobody able to find a compass."*

government that unequivocally endorsed chiropractic as more safe, efficacious and cost-effective than traditional medical approaches to back problems. About a year later the U.S. Agency for Health Care Policy and Research issued its guidelines for treatment of low back pain, recommending spinal manipulation. All of a sudden research favorable to chiropractic was splashing around the boat like a school of happy dolphins.

The *Associated Press*, which had pasted chiropractic for causing strokes, now proclaimed that government-sponsored research had vindicated chiropractic over medical doctors. Of course, the AHCPR Guideline hadn't mentioned chiropractic, but the chiropractors were happy enough, albeit leery of that weasel-word expression "spinal manipulation." Still, most would take what they could get. Could the eggheads, who had been quietly doing their research – which hardly anybody noticed and even fewer were willing to pay for – end up steering the profession to the paradise shores of economic security?

Something else. The *New England Journal of Medicine* conveyed the stunning news that during one year people in the United States, especially those relatively well educated and with higher incomes, made 37 million more visits to alternative care providers than to all primary care physicians. A social sea change was evidently underway. Millions were reading or seeing on TV the thoughts of Deepak Chopra, M.D., whose mind-body thinking parallels some aspects of chiropractic. Was society ready to adopt the wellness philosophy central to chiropractic for 100 years? Would chiropractors be able to articulate it to their economic advantage?

It was in that stormy, confusing, yet exciting atmosphere that the Chiropractic Centennial Foundation began organizing the commemoration of the profession's 100th anniversary. When planning began in the 1980s, probably little more was envisioned than a sort of profession-wide college homecoming. But times had changed. This 100th anniversary held enormous symbolic and practical potential. Would the Grand Celebration prove to be a coming-out party... or a wake?

Decisions, decisions, decisions for Dr. Roger Hulsebus, Dr. Marilyn P. Smith, Donald M. Petersen Jr., and others

# CCF brings together some of profession's top organizers

The Centennial planners were selected by their respective organizations for their proven success, experience and commitment. Although changes in personnel occurred during the duration of the Chiropractic Centennial Foundation, an organizational chart retained in the master planning book listed officers and committee members as follows:

William F. Holmberg, D.C.

Kerwin P. Winkler, D.C.

Michael J. Hulsebus, D.C.

Louis P. Latimer, D.C.

Carl S. Cleveland, III, D.C.

Glenda Wiese, M.A.

Marilyn P. Smith, D.C.

## Board of Trustees

Officers – William F. Holmberg, D.C., president; Kerwin P. Winkler, D.C., vice president; Michael J. Hulsebus, D.C., vice president; Louis P. Latimer, D.C., secretary; Roger D. Hulsebus, D.C., treasurer.

Trustees – Carl S. Cleveland, III, D.C.; Glenda Wiese, M.A.; Marilyn P. Smith, D.C.; David A. Chapman-Smith, Esq.; Donald M. Petersen, Jr.

Administrative staff – David B. Anderson, D.C., administrative assistant; Tom Tiemeier, assistant treasurer; Mary McCubbin, Annette Ven Horst and Marian Williams, assistant secretaries.

## Board Committees

Continuing education – Carl S. Cleveland, III, D.C., chairman; David A. Chapman-Smith, Esq.; Glenda Wiese, M.A.; Marilyn P. Smith, D.C.; Patrick Keefe, Sr., D.C.

Entertainment – Roger D. Hulsebus, D.C., co-chairman; David A. Chapman-Smith, Esq., co-chairman; Guy Riekeman, D.C.

Planning & budget – Rick McMichael, D.C., chairman; Donald M. Petersen, Jr.; Rick Flaherty; Glenda Wiese, M.A.

Registration – Donald M. Petersen, Jr., chairman; Roger D. Hulsebus, D.C.; Louis P. Latimer, D.C.; David A. Chapman-Smith, Esq.; Jerilynn Kaibel, D.C.

Commemorative book – Michael J. Hulsebus, D.C., chairman; Donald M. Petersen, Jr.; Juan Nodarse; Rick Flaherty.

Honors & awards – Louis P. Latimer, D.C., co-chairman; Marilyn P. Smith, D.C., co-chairperson.

## Advisory Committee

Donald M. Petersen, Jr., chairman.

Celebration exhibits & events – Jerilynn Kaibel, D.C., chairperson; Edward C. Williams, D.C.; Karl Parker, D.C.

Communications – Juan Nodarse, chairman; Terry Rondberg, D.C.; Donald M. Petersen, Jr.

Media projects – Guy Riekeman, D.C., chairman; Gary Street, D.C.; Louis Sportelli, D.C.; Stephen D. Eckstone, Ph.D.

Development – Rick Flaherty, chairman; Kent Greenawalt, Arlan Fuhr, D.C.

Special projects – Michael Schroeder, Esq., chairman; Rick McMichael, D.C.; Sid E. Williams, D.C.

Roger D. Hulsebus, D.C.

David A. Chapman-Smith, Esq.

Donald M. Petersen, Jr.

Jerilynn Kaibel, D.C.

Guy Riekeman, D.C.

Rick Flaherty

Frank Bemis, D.C.

James Winterstein, D.C.

D. Brent Owens, D.C.

Patrick Keefe, D.C.

William Rehm, D.C.

Gary Auerbach, D.C.

David Anderson, D.C.

Mary McCubbin

Marian Williams

Annette Ven Horst

# From the start, celebration aims to be profession-wide

Planning for the Chiropractic Centennial went back at least to 1984, when a committee at Palmer College was appointed to plan for a commemoration. The person appointed to chair that committee was Dr. William F. Holmberg, a successful Rock Island, Illinois, chiropractor, who would be remembered as chairman of the committee that raised money for the Wilk anti-trust suit. A report to the Palmer board of trustees in January 1984 also noted: "We are setting aside a contingency fund to be available for use in celebrating the Centennial of Chiropractic (1995)."

Early in the planning it was recognized that the celebration should be not just a Palmer College event but for the entire profession. To facilitate profession-wide involvement and ensure all activities would be generic to the whole profession, the Chiropractic Centennial Foundation (CCF) was formed as a 501(c)3 non-profit organization. Trusteeships available at $5,000 per year for five years were extended to national organizations representing the majority of the profession, and *ex-officio* levels of involvement were offered to all the chiropractic colleges and to state, country, provincial and other professional associations. By the end of the Centennial year, nearly 120 associations and institutions had joined the CCF, an accomplishment that itself merited a celebration, given the profession's fragmented history.

## The CCF adopted the following mission statement:

*The Chiropractic Centennial Foundation maintains as its mission and purpose responsibility for planning, coordination and effective administration and implementation of programs and events for the profession's Centennial year, 1995, providing for:*

1. *Recognition of the profession's history, dissemination of current scientific and educational advancements as well as future impact on the world's health.*
2. *Encouragement of profession-wide participation in Centennial events.*
3. *National and international visibility recognizing chiropractic as an important component of the health care community.*
4. *Recognition of and commitment to research within the chiropractic profession.*

Along with its mission statement, the CCF set five goals. Here they are along with projects originally listed to accomplish them.

*Celebrate the Centennial of Chiropractic:* Kickoff 9/94, Rose Parade float 1/95, Washington celebration 7/95, Davenport celebration 9/95, college celebrations, state association celebrations, individual D.C. celebrations, honors and awards.

*Educate and inform the public about chiropractic:* docudrama, national marketing campaign, general publicity, special media projects, stamp/seal, educational program for schools.

*Increase awareness of our heritage:* book – *Chiropractic: An Illustrated History*; tapes – pioneers, docudrama, historical markers, historic display, oral histories, calendar.

*Unify the profession through involvement in Centennial activities:* Kickoff 9/94, Centennial newsletter, commemorative book, constituency meetings, memberships, sponsorships, "who's who," essays on chiropractic's future, celebration events, individual D.C. celebrations.

*Encourage and support chiropractic research:* research grants/awards, scientific symposium and continuing education, proceedings.

A few of those projects never came about – the U.S. chiropractic postage stamp being the most notable example – but the vast majority did, a credit to the CCF board and its advisory committee. The planning process had its ups and downs, but, all things considered, went remarkably well. The assembled leaders, some of whom invested many hours of their time and personal resources, all shared the original vision of a Celebration of which the entire profession could be proud.

# Fantastic! Call DACS and tell him da-da-da

Dr. William F. Holmberg cut a swath through the Centennial with his sense of humor and earthy communication style.

For one thing, he had a knack for shortening or altering fellow CCF planners' names. Carl S. Cleveland, III, was "C-3." David A. Chapman-Smith was "DACS." Holmberg's secretary, Mary McCubbin, was always "Mary Mac." Juan Nodarse, one of Holmberg's most trusted advisers, was "Juan Don."

When he'd hang up the phone, his closing was a cheerful, "See ya!" and with select people, "Love ya, Daddy."

He also had a habit of placing accents in unexpected places. D.D. Palmer had the accent on the second D., not Deé-dee but Dee-deé. Jerilynn Kaibel was not Jerí-lynn but Jeri-lynń. Documentary was not documén-tary but documen-tarý.

Holmberg was always "lighting a fire" under this or that one who wasn't moving "their bubble butt" fast enough. When he wanted to indicate that maybe somebody else would think there was more to say but he didn't, he'd end his sentence with "da-da-da," as in: "Don Petersen says there's a mistake in the damn registration form and all hell's breaking loose da-da-da." The most "das" anybody recalls is seven or eight in a single string, which he would spit out like a machine gun.

Perhaps the single expression most often associated with him was the word "fantastic!" Things didn't just go well, they went "fantastic!" It was more than a mannerism. It reflected the upbeat attitude that kept him going no matter what.

A mountain of paperwork and responsibility for Dr. William F. Holmberg

# Differing perspectives, one common objective

An impressive and fascinating group they were, these leaders of the profession who comprised the Chiropractic Centennial Foundation. Here were representatives of the American Chiropractic Association (ACA), International Chiropractors Association (ICA), Association of Chiropractic Colleges (ACC), World Federation of Chiropractic (WFC), National Board of Chiropractic Examiners (NBCE), Association for the History of Chiropractic (AHC) and Palmer College working for common cause. The board meetings were plenty lively, with lots of vigorous debate, but the planners generally worked together well despite disparate philosophical perspectives.

Consider first the CCF president, Dr. William F. Holmberg. "He comes across like a good ol' boy from Alabama," Dr. Guy Riekeman said about him, "and then you find out he's as smooth as they come." Dr. Holmberg's mock-redneck style only thinly disguised considerable people skills. His sense of humor and rough-language sarcasm kept the planners loose. This was a person who learned chiropractic politics watching B.J. Palmer, who was instrumental in fundraising for the court case that freed the profession from the AMA's conspiratorial hammerlock, and

Trustees Carl S. Cleveland III and Glenda Wiese, at yet another meeting

who was warm-hearted and courageous enough to steer an *ad hoc* organization with more than its share of sizable egos. David A. Chapman-Smith, Esq., described Dr. Holmberg's interactions with the board as "a father presiding over a bunch of unruly teenagers."

Dr. Kerwin P. Winkler, vice president, represented the ACA. He has a patrician's demeanor, balanced, kind and cheerful, but another chiropractor with fire in the belly for the profession. His dignified presence

at the meetings helped keep things on a high plane. He was frustrated by the failure of his chiropractic postage stamp project, which ran into a stone wall of bureaucratic indifference.

Dr. Michael Hulsebus, a successful practitioner and the trustee for the ICA, brought an engaging enthusiasm, especially for the celebratory aspects of the Centennial. Throughout the meetings he raised questions that helped clarify the issues. Like others on the board, he contributed an evident love for the profession, which in his case was a family tradition. His father, Dr. Robert Hulsebus, helped effect chiropractic legislative victories in Illinois and nationally.

Dr. Louis P. Latimer, the trustee for the National Board of Chiropractic Examiners, is quiet, friendly, down to earth, exhibiting a wide range of knowledge about the people and the history of the profession. His contacts were a valuable resource for the CCF. At the New Year's Eve party in Beverly Hills he seemed a bit miffed because the band didn't invite him up to play the drums. The next day at the Rose Bowl game he was grinning from ear to ear. He hails from Pennsylvania, and Penn State was winning handily.

Dr. Roger Hulsebus, Michael's older brother and a trustee representing Palmer College, served as treasurer and proved to be another forceful presence on the board. His emphasis on chiropractic philosophy put him at an opposite pole from Chapman-Smith, but the two shared a commitment to making the Centennial a success. Chapman-Smith remarked, "Our difference is in emphasis on philosophy and science, but it takes two wings to fly."

Dr. Carl S. Cleveland, III, a fourth-generation chiropractor and president of the Cleveland Colleges, was the trustee for the Association of Chiropractic Colleges. Mild-mannered, genteel and always impeccably dressed, Dr. Cleveland could have stepped out of *Gentlemen's Quarterly*. Reports had it that one night at a constituency meeting he was issued a fund-raising challenge to name all 90 people in the room and did it. When the other board members talked about him, they often used the word "depth."

Didn't Glenda Wiese, the AHC trustee, have enough to do as co-author (with Dennis Peterson) of a big and enlightening Centennial book, *Chiropractic: An Illustrated History*? Evidently not, for she ended up steering several other history-related projects too, including the historical exhibit and the historical markers. Quick to deprecate herself as "an Iowa farm girl," she demonstrated ability to manage details until a project was done.

Dr. Marilyn Smith, another trustee representing Palmer College, served on the continuing education and honors & awards committees. Like a parent setting a positive tone for her children, Dr. Smith added enthusiasm and an optimistic attitude. Her warmth and kindly sense of humor helped preserve a friendly atmosphere at the CCF meetings.

Chapman-Smith is the lawyer who successfully represented the chiropractic profession in the extensive New Zealand Commission hearings and the editor/publisher of the *Chiropractic Report*, a widely read review of research and professional issues. Chapman-Smith, who hasn't lost his New Zealand accent since moving to Canada, is quintessentially urbane, knowledgeable and a master of understatement. As the trustee representing the World Federation of Chiropractic, he brought an expansive world view to the CCF, advocating for international representation in Centennial activities.

About Donald M. Petersen, Jr., once Chapman-Smith quipped, "He lacks commitment." Of course, everybody involved with the Centennial knew nobody had more. When you watched Petersen stuffing flowers on the Rose Parade float, or sweating and racing to break down boxes at the Washington, D.C., gala registration, you saw the standard-setter for Centennial hard work. He headed up the tough job of registration as well as the advisory committee, which included exhibits, communications, media projects, development and special projects. His newspaper, *Dynamic Chiropractic*, was the main Centennial information conduit to the profession. He was also a master facilitator, the one they called "Corridor Man" because he was often out in the hall heading off difficulties.

Dr. Jerilynn Kaibel, honored as the ACA's "Chiropractor of the Year," was chairperson of the Celebration exhibits & events committee, bringing a type-A personality and exceptional dedication to all her projects. She was usually in the middle of the give and take at the board meetings. There was a report that somebody had given her a live pig as a joke, and she kept it and drove around in her Camaro with the pig sitting next to her. That sort of rambunctiousness aside, Dr. Kaibel was described by other CCF planners as "a super volunteer," "experienced," "fully capable," and "probably America's First Lady of Chiropractic."

Dr. Guy Riekeman played a multifaceted role, leading the media projects committee, appearing as one of the Centennial's most popular speakers and devoting himself as the director/producer (and fund-raiser) for the chiropractic documentary. In contrast to Dr. Cleveland's sartorial splendor, Riekeman often dressed casually at the Centennial meetings. More an idealist than a pragmatist, Riekeman's always mild manner didn't hide his ardent convictions about where the profession ought to head.

Rick Flaherty, of Leander Health Technologies, who headed up the all-important development committee, brought to the party a salesman's drive

**Some Centennial promotional shirts and caps**

and an Irishman's cantankerousness and sense of humor. Although not a chiropractor, he worked creatively and effectively to raise money to support the Centennial. "Getting involved requires giving up something," Flaherty observed, and he and his wife, Cathy, were seen giving their time, talents and seemingly inexhaustible energy at every turn. "That Rick Flaherty," Holmberg said a dozen times if once, "is one hell of a hard worker."

The Centennial planners complemented each other nicely. All had strengths and made valuable contributions. Morale was low after the disappointing attendance at the Washington, D.C., gala, but the well-supported Davenport events helped heal the wounds. When the Centennial was all over, Holmberg would still refer to the CCF *team* and didn't feel he was stretching things.

# Budget comes out OK after million-dollar scare

When the Chiropractic Centennial Foundation trustees set out to manage the Centennial activities, they asked Rick McMichael, D.C., to help them determine a budget.

"Obviously, we were in unmapped territory from the beginning," recalls Dr. William Holmberg, who said that in their initial budget planning "we just threw out numbers and tried to guess if they were anywhere close." With McMichael's help in facilitating the budgeting process, the group established five budgetary divisions, each with its own sources of income.

Division #1: Membership/Administrative Operations. The original trusteeships and *ex officio* involvement by associations and colleges were projected to bring in $331,500, a wash with the expenses of administrative operations.

Division #2: National Marketing/Media Projects. Projects included the public relations campaign, documentary, telemarketing, support staff, Rose Parade float, oral histories and other projects. Money was to come from corporate sponsors and other donors. Initial projections were between $2,500,000 and $5,025,000 in income and roughly the same in expenses.

Division #3: Registration/Celebrations/Continuing Education. Income there came from registration fees, optional events and interest on the money. Projects in this category included facilities, entertainment, grants and awards, the kickoff and others. Possible income was estimated at $3,050,000, about $280,000 over projected expenses.

Division #4: Exhibits. An estimated $1,200,000 was expected from exhibit fees, sponsor portions and interest. Expenses were expected to be considerably less, at $440,000.

Division #5: Self-funded Projects. The newsletter, product sales, licensing, commemorative book, *Illustrated History* and other projects were expected to bring in $505,000, with expenses of only $230,000.

The total "highest possible budget estimate," adding up the division numbers came to $10,786,500, with projected expenses (highest possible) at $9,533,000.

Rick McMichael, D.C.

The final budget would come in at about half that. Figures at the end of the Centennial year (December 31, 1995), with some expenses and income still to come in, showed $5,819,553.28 in income and $5,499,459.18 in disbursements and $320,094.10 in cash on hand.

Why the difference between what was expected and the final result? Less than anticipated support from the profession.

"At one point we were hearing reports from a telemarketing firm we hired that we could expect 10,000 people at the Washington gala and 25,000 people at Davenport," Holmberg said. "The reality turned out to be 2,128 (including about 1,100 D.C.'s) in Washington and 5,435 (including about

Historian Russell Gibbons, conferring with David A. Chapman-Smith

3,000 D.C.'s) in Davenport." Those telemarketers also indicated considerable additional money in donor pledges. When the pledges didn't come in and the CCF sent letters to follow up, some of the doctors claimed they had never made the pledges.

As the Washington gala drew near, the CCF board could see they might fall as much as one million dollars in the red. They were panicked, but there wasn't much they could do. "I've never felt so drained,"

Holmberg said later. "The problem was we had already booked expensive entertainment and presenters and a high-priced Convention Center and incurred other expenses by the time we discovered the attendance and pledge figures were fictitious."

To bring the budget back in line, expenses had to be cut for the Davenport gala and other areas. For instance, plans to bring in the Beach Boys or another top group for a concert had to be canceled. "We also were helped because the actual costs in Davenport turned out to be less than we had anticipated, just the opposite from Washington," Holmberg said. The rest of the difference was made up by post-Washington donations from the Life Colleges, ACC,

ACA, NCMIC, Foot Levelers and Educational Funding Service.

The idea of going to Washington, D.C., seemed like a good idea at the time. It would take the strength of the profession and plop it under the noses of the politicians in Washington. It would be a prestigious setting for the scientific conference to be complemented by the back-to-the-birthplace celebration in Davenport.

"If I had it to do over again," Holmberg said, "I would have pushed for a venue in a place, like, say, Chicago, where people could take day trips to The Fountainhead. Whatever the case, I think most of us would opt for a single combined event."

## Financial procedures

With the big money involved, estimated at $10 million at one point, the CCF was scrupulous about its financial procedures. Expenses had to be approved by both a committee chairman and the president, each bonded for $1,000,000. Vouchers were written with the president's signature and that of the assistant treasurer. Checks written per vouchers were

signed by either the president or the assistant treasurer. Bookkeeping was handled by Alexis Vanderhorn of Palmer College, with accounting reports submitted monthly to the CCF board. Annual independent audits were done by the firm of McGladrey & Pullen.

*"The reality turned out to be 2,128 in Washington and 5,435 in Davenport."*

A painting commissioned for Centennial promotion

# Corporate sponsors show confidence in profession

There would have been no Grand Celebration without the generosity of corporate sponsors. Here are 11 of those companies, two Elite Club Super Sponsors (at least $300,000 donations) and nine in the Platinum Club Crown category (at least $50,000), with some expressions by these who put their money where their mouth is.

The National Chiropractic Mutual Insurance Co. (NCMIC) was one of the two Elite Club Super Sponsors. Dr. Arnold Cianciulli said: "NCMIC is celebrating our 50th year this year, and it was put together by some very visionary doctors of chiropractic. It was designed to service the doctors because they realized early on that we needed to have an insurance company because of so much prejudice and bias that existed in those days against the profession. ..." With regard to the reason behind his company's sizable contribution, Dr. Cianciulli said: "We wanted to make sure that we showed the entire world that NCMIC, which is involved with over 50 percent of the practicing doctors of chiropractic, believes very strongly that our future is very bright and that some of the apparent problems with managed care and other things of this nature will resolve themselves very favorably for the chiropractic profession."

Standard Process, Inc., a maker of nutritional supplements, was the other Elite Club Super Sponsor. Mary Wisniewski, vice president of marketing, said the company's donation "is a big thank you, mostly, for turning us into the leaders in our industry. Seventy-six percent of our customers are chiropractors, and without their help we wouldn't be who we are today." Speaking about chiropractors' future she said: "They are going to be more and more the mainstream answer to health problems and health maintenance. We are going to rely on them for that kind of guidance."

Foot Levelers, Inc., a well-known manufacturer of orthotic devices, was listed as a Platinum Club Crown sponsor although the company donated several times the minimum $50,000 amount for that category. Foot Levelers shared seminar proceeds with the Centennial ($200,000) and chiropractic colleges ($200,000) throughout the Centennial year. President Kent Greenawalt said, "We have always tried to give back to this profession, which has been extremely good to us." He expressed optimism about chiropractic: "Every trend I can see shows that people are moving in our direction. People are coming to realize that what we have to offer is really one of the best health care options. We're very optimistic."

Leander Health Technologies, a Platinum sponsor, is the company of Rick Flaherty, who did so much to raise corporate money for the Centennial. Here's how he explained his involvement: "I think this company has become one of the most visual chiropractic suppliers, and is known for its quality products and unparalleled service. I felt that if I could put the same qualities that I brought to this company into the Centennial and help spread some of this into the profession, then we could increase the viability of the profession and make the chiropractic profession known around the country."

Dr. Guy Riekeman's Quest Alliance, another Platinum Club sponsor, trains chiropractors, Dr. Riekeman said, "for the changing health care field. We wanted to produce staff training that would accommodate more long-term wellness, care-oriented business and practices." The future of chiropractic? "I think our profession has a major decision

to make about whether we want to stay as a sub-specialty within the current medical philosophy of treating problems after they show up, or whether we want to become a leading profession in the evolving wellness care systems."

Back Talk Systems, Inc., a publisher of patient education materials, was also a Platinum sponsor. Founder William Esteb noted: "Chiropractic is all we do here. Since 1989, Back Talk Systems, Inc., has produced a variety of videos, posters, brochures and practice growth aids that are subluxation-based, and embrace the diversity of the chiropractic profession while reflecting our culture's growing emphasis on visual communications." He offered this perspective: "The real challenge will be how clearly and how articulately individual doctors can explain chiro-practic to their patients."

Eastman Kodak, a Platinum Club sponsor, saw an appropriate tie-in with the chiropractic profession because the Centennial year of chiropractic was also the 100th anniversary of x-rays. A spokesman noted, "Also, at the tail end of 1994 we introduced a new product line specifically for this part of the market, including chiropractors, called clinic select x-ray films, which are high quality films available at an affordable price. We wanted to highlight and create awareness around that product line through our sponsorship of the chiropractic Centennial."

Grady Miars, director of sales and marketing for Bennett X-ray Technologies, a Platinum sponsor, said: "The chiropractic profession has been very good to us, and we wanted to support chiropractic in its Centennial, a significant event and milestone in the profession." His company displayed digital x-ray equipment, which does without film, process-ing or chemistry, a process expected to be the wave of the future in imaging.

Core Products International, another Platinum-level sponsor, manufactures orthopedic soft goods. President Phillip Mattison: "(We) decided that by using some portion of our advertising dollars to sponsor the Centennial that we'd be giving some-thing back to the industry, which we felt was extremely important. We also felt we'd be doing a good job of reinforcing our logo recognition with-in the industry."

Chattanooga Group, Inc., a manufacturer of tables and traction equipment, explained its Platinum sponsorship as a "customer-oriented commitment." Tom Voight, general manager, observed: "We felt that (the Centennial) was a point of unity for the profession, something for the profession to take sat-isfaction in. It is neutral ground. I've been con-cerned for a number of years about some of the divisiveness that goes on in the profession. ... I feel that chiropractic really has an opportunity to come out much stronger over the next couple of years than it realized it could, even as recently as six to eight months ago."

Platinum sponsor ProGroup's Kevin Benedict, sales manager of the software company, said: "As the leader in chiropractic software, we felt it was our responsibility to lead by example and support the Centennial Celebration. ... The future of the chiro-practic profession will require that chiropractors have improved human relations and better practice-building skills in order to compete with other health care professions. Chiropractors will need to have better training in business and marketing."

*"We have always tried to give back to this profes-sion, which has been extremely good to us."*

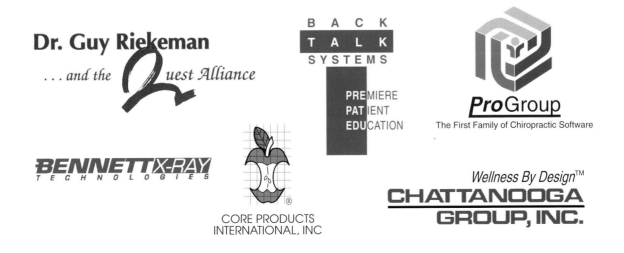

13

# Centennial celebrations here, there, everywhere

Many chiropractic colleges and professional associations in North America not only jumped on the bandwagon to support the Chiropractic Centennial Foundation with displays and receptions at the galas, but also organized their own Centennial opportunities to tell the chiropractic story both directly and indirectly. The CCF reported these examples.

The Arizona Association of Chiropractic organized a memorabilia display for its 1995 convention, including old black and white photographs dating back to the early days of chiropractic. Lynn Moreno, spokesperson for the Association, said one particularly interesting item was a leather-bound cash ledger listing payment of association dues in 1934 – when they were $2 a year.

Activities by the Colorado Chiropractic Association ranged from birthday cakes at patient appreciation nights to promotional kits to a mobile educational trailer, according to Martha Gorman, the Association's public relations director. The 42-foot trailer, available to doctors throughout the state, was outfitted with computers, touch-screen diagnostics and ultrasound technology to tell the story of the past, present and future of chiropractic. The

*"Our campaign theme is Chiropractic: The Backbone of America."*

**Many chiropractic colleges held their own Centennial celebrations**

trailer traveled the rodeo circuit and made an appearance at the 1995 Colorado State Fair.

The North Carolina Chiropractic Association jumped on the publicity bandwagon early with its own committee and spokespeople to create local interest in the chiropractic story. John Flynn, D.C., said: "We're pumping it up in North Carolina. We already have in place a public relations committee to handle promotions in our state. Our campaign theme is 'Chiropractic: The Backbone of America.' We're using the CCF press kits to dovetail national efforts with local publicity here in North Carolina."

The Nevada State Chiropractic Association spurred state and national legislators from Nevada to recognize chiropractic in four proclamations read in both state legislatures and the U.S. House and Senate, becoming part of the Congressional Record.

The Ohio State Chiropractic Association set a fund-raising goal of $150,000. "We've made an effort to go out to each district and bring the Centennial to them."

Canadian Memorial Chiropractic College events included a ceremonial raising of the CMCC flag, a "Neighboring Institutions" luncheon and a party to celebrate D.D. Palmer's 150th birthday and the 50th anniversary of CMCC.

Cleveland Chiropractic College of Kansas City adopted an 1895 theme for its Homecoming '94, "As it was in the beginning... of chiropractic." Highlights of the event included a costume affair and a display of clothing worn by Kansas Citians during that era. Alumni from the Cleveland College at Los Angeles met with alumni from Kansas City for a Centennial get-together in Las Vegas.

Life College held its Centennial celebration on Monday, September 18, with a day-long program on its Atlanta, Georgia, campus. Atlanta residents were greeted by morning newspapers containing ads commending the Centennial. The 1995 Centennial class had its commencement exercises in Life's new $2 million stadium complex. A highlight of Life's festivities was the appearance of actor David Richards as D.D. Palmer.

Life West at San Lorenzo, California, launched its Festival '94 with a Centennial birthday cake and picnic. Sid E. Williams, D.C., the college's founder, appeared at a gathering in July 1995, encouraging students to hold on to their philosophical beliefs despite ridicule. Life West also put on a "Health Extravaganza and Life Celebration" in August 1995. Featured speaker was Dr. Guy Riekeman, president of Quest

Publicity efforts included a week of chiropractic segments on a local New York radio station. Serge Nerli, D.C., the Association's president, said: "D.C.'s must come together to share the Centennial message with the public and our patients. People don't understand our longevity – we've been around for a century, and we're going to lead the way for health care in the next 100 years."

Northwestern College of Chiropractic joined up with the Minnesota Chiropractic Association for the 1995 homecoming and unveiled a special birthday cake in recognition of the profession's 100th birthday.

Palmer College of Chiropractic organized a special Centennial program for students who couldn't afford to attend the Davenport gala. Palmer also sponsored a major feature of the Davenport gala, "An Evening with Ray Charles – a Salute to the Palmer Family." It also was aggressive about linking Centennial interest with publicity about itself as chiropractic's founding college.

Palmer College of Chiropractic West celebrated the Centennial in August 1995 with speakers discussing the history and future of the profession. Dr. Guy Riekeman again was a featured speaker. Palmer West student Joel Kinch presented the CCF with a check for $2,500 contributed by nearly 70 percent of the student body.

Parker College of Chiropractic used a Centennial theme for its annual alumni fund-raising event and planned several promotional events to spread the word about chiropractic in the Dallas, Texas, area.

Sherman College of Straight Chiropractic organized its 1995 Lyceum as a Centennial Jubilee, with speakers, seminars and workshops on its campus in Spartanburg, South Carolina.

Texas Chiropractic College's major fund-raising event, the annual Mardi Gras Gala, commemorated 100 years of chiropractic.

Western States Chiropractic College organized a traveling historical library display depicting how far chiropractic has come and the role Western States played in that development.

Alliance Seminars and chair of the Centennial Foundation's committee for media projects.

Logan College of Chiropractic combined the college's 60th anniversary with the Centennial.

National College of Chiropractic dedicated its 1995 Homecoming to the Centennial, with the theme, "Celebrating a Century of Chiropractic." The program included recognized chiropractic historians.

New York Chiropractic College activities included bulletin boards on campus and Centennial-oriented events for alumni and friends of the college.

# Chiropractic media get word to the profession

The chiropractic media, including association and college publications, helped spread the word about the Centennial. They ran the CCF news releases, frequently provided free space for Centennial advertising, communicated details about Centennial activities involving their respective associations and institutions and rallied chiropractors and chiropractic students.

The editor of *Dynamic Chiropractic*, Donald M. Petersen, Jr., who worked tirelessly on the Centennial prior to and during the Centennial year, made sure his publication gave thorough editorial and photographic coverage on almost every aspect. In addition, *Dynamic Chiropractic* regularly provided free advertising space to communicate details about Centennial schedules, registration and programs. Page 4 of each issue was devoted to the Centennial.

"It is hard to imagine we would have gotten the word out without the help of Don Petersen," said Dr. William Holmberg, CCF president. "This profession owes him and his staff a debt we probably can never repay just in free – and accurate – publicity alone, not to mention all their work behind the scenes."

The publications of both the American Chiropractic Association and the International Chiropractors Association also regularly devoted huge blocks of print space to news of the Centennial. They also contained appeals from the leadership to support the Centennial.

An especially powerful appeal came from Kerwin P. Winkler, D.C., ACA Governor, District I (and chairman of the ACA Board of Governors), who served on the CCF board. He outlined the many accomplishments of the CCF and the progress of the profession over the century. He also boldly took to task the individual chiropractors who reneged on their pledges or failed to show up at the galas.

Association and college publications devoted huge blocks of space to Centennial promotion and coverage

The editor of the *American Chiropractor* magazine, Lana Stewart, announced that chiropractic pioneers, beginning with Charles Wood, D.C., would be featured throughout the year.

The *Texas Journal of Chiropractic* and the *PCC Alumni News* of Palmer College were among publications that ran the CCF graphic announcing the Centennial on their covers. The "Imagine" artwork featured a large "head shot" of D.D. Palmer and a specially commissioned illustration.

The *Digest of Chiropractic Economics* regularly reported on the progress of the fund-raising and other aspects. One bit in the January/February 1994 issue was typical of the emotional appeal that the *Digest* and other publications frequently conveyed. The item quoted two Delaware chiropractors, Drs. Allen Foster and Debra Hobbs, who donated $5,000: "It's important to remember the struggles of those who came before us. We reap the benefits of their fight, and it's up to us to support the profession of today and tomorrow."

*Chiropractic Products*, besides regularly carrying Centennial news, put out a special edition in December 1994 featuring products from the Chiropractic Centennial Store on the cover and inside. The magazine explained the licensing agreement between the CCF and Max Pack, the Cleveland, Ohio, company responsible for manufacturing and distributing Centennial products. "As part of the licensing agreement between Max Pack and the CCF, a substantial portion of all proceeds from the sale of licensed items is returned to the Centennial Foundation. The proceeds are then used to help create a national campaign to advance understanding of chiropractic, educate the public on the benefits of chiropractic, increase awareness of chiropractic's heritage, unify the profession through Centennial activities and encourage and support chiropractic research."

# Centennial promotion – read it, wear it, etc.

One of the ways the CCF planners reached and energized the profession was through a slick, four-color tabloid that reported on donors and the progress of fund-raising, the media campaign, the progress of the documentary, college events, and many other aspects of the Grand Celebration.

The several issues contained features on the Centennial leaders and other chiropractors who were demonstrating their commitment to the profession. The publication also included the advertising for all the Max Pack promotional items and advance registration forms and other practical information about attending. Rick Flaherty and Donald M. Petersen, Jr., helped coordinate that project, working with Bawdens & Associates, a Davenport advertising/public relations agency.

## T-shirts, paper weights, golf balls...

Conveying the Centennial message was not only accomplished by formal newspaper, radio and television coverage but also by an impressive range of promotional items sold to members of the profession to be worn or displayed.

Apparel with the Centennial logo or message included T-shirts, golf shirts, sweat shirts, baseball jerseys, rugby shirts, tank tops, shorts, sweaters, warm-up suits and jackets, as well as items for children and infants, including dresses, shirts and terry cloth bibs.

Jewelry, desk pieces and other Centennial promotional items included stick pins, men's and women's rings, watches, lapel pins, a variety of coffee mugs,

Telling the story took many forms

18

engraved pens, luggage tags, walnut, marble and brass desk sets, paper weights, signature golf balls and golf towels, gold embossed labels, and key chains.

Other special commemorative items included a set of nine commemorative buttons, five cloisonné metal pins, two minted silver coins, Rose Parade posters, wall plaques and collector's plates.

Purchase of those items gave chiropractors and their families opportunities both to contribute to Centennial fund raising and to show their pride in their professional calling.

## Centennial Fridays

About the first of June 1995 the Chiropractic Centennial Foundation declared every Friday up until the grand Centennial finale in Davenport as "Chiropractic Centennial Day."

Chiropractors and supporters of the profession everywhere were encouraged to wear T-shirts, sweatshirts, polo shirts or other outerwear with the official Centennial logo to show the public that 1995 was chiropractic's 100th anniversary.

# Kicking Off the Centennial Year

*Spirits were high, plans were jelling, and the leadership was in place to direct the chiropractic profession to what could truly be a Grand Celebration of its Centennial. Suddenly the focus was not on professional differences but on chiropractic's 100 years of healing success and its potential for a glorious future. The kickoff was nothing but positive.*

### Kicking things off – filling the mind, touching the heart

The excitement was almost palpable as about 300 chiropractic leaders gathered September 17, 1994, in Davenport's RiverCenter to kick off the Centennial.

Jim Griswold, D.C., representing the Michigan Chiropractic Society, summed up the general feeling: "Well, this is it. After 100 years, this is our time to come together and express with one voice what chiropractic means to humankind."

The Centennial kickoff was to motivate and prepare the leaders of the profession to meet the lofty CCF goals, including the most ambitious one, what Dr. Griswold and kickoff co-chairman Roger Hulsebus, D.C., called speaking "with one voice."

After enthusiastic presentations by committee chairmen, inspiring luncheon speeches orchestrated by Dr. Carl S. Cleveland, III, and a rousing evening with comedian Allan Thicke and Dr. Guy Riekeman's multi-media program, everybody agreed the kickoff was a great beginning.

In an opening session, an excited CCF president Dr. William F. Holmberg, happily welcomed the attendees: "We have the cream of the chiropractic profession here!" Seventeen chiropractic colleges were represented, as well as all the major national associations – "the alphabet associations" – and all the state associations. "And I'm just tickled to death!"

In planning meetings throughout the day, committee chairmen gave progress reports and conducted workshops on each facet of the Grand Celebration.

> *"We have the cream of the chiropractic profession here!"*

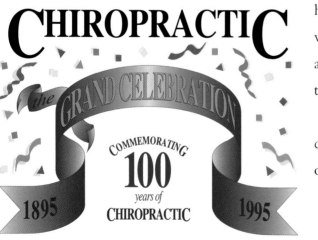

CHIROPRACTIC

the GRAND CELEBRATION

COMMEMORATING **100** years of CHIROPRACTIC

1895    1995

**The kickoff was filled with both substance and symbolism**

Glenda Wiese outlined historical projects, including publication of the book *Chiropractic: An Illustrated History*, creation of the historical exhibit, commissioning of original oil paintings and the placing of the historical markers. Marilyn Smith, D.C., and Sofya Belair later showed college representatives how college booth displays would be set up at the Washington, D.C., and Davenport galas.

Rick Flaherty explained the fund-raising activities and encouraged everyone to give at least $100 to the chiropractic cause. Don Petersen, Jr., highlighted the plans for the chiropractic float in the Rose Parade and the New Year's Eve party. A model of the chiropractic float was on display.

Juan Nodarse laid out the public relations strategy, which would involve not only the efforts by two agencies to spread the word both inside and outside the profession but also a grassroots effort across the country. Attendees learned how they could have an effective share.

**Rick Flaherty, Sofya Belair and Glenda Wiese**

Guy Riekeman, D.C., explained various media projects, including the limited edition audio tapes and the chiropractic documentary. It was the first of several inspiring presentations from Dr. Riekeman throughout the Centennial year. He would emerge from the Centennial widely recognized as one of chiropractic's most passionate and eloquent spokesmen.

During breaks, chiropractors were invited to be interviewed for hometown radio news releases. For example, Dr. Cal Whitworth, president of the American Black Chiropractic Association, was interviewed about lost work time because of back pain and the importance of seeing a chiropractor. The tape was then sent to his hometown of Boston. The hometown radio releases proved to be one of the most successful of Centennial public relations efforts.

Out in the lobby of Davenport's RiverCenter chiropractors and their spouses bought golf shirts, T-shirts, caps and other paraphernalia, and swapped greetings, memories and best wishes. Camera shutters clicked frequently.

The future of the profession was a common topic. One young Logan College graduate said, "I think this is a fine time to be a chiropractor. I'm excited."

She wasn't the only one. Especially after the luncheon and later the Alan Thicke performance and multi-media presentations, just about everybody was excited.

Jerilynn S. Kaibel, D.C., a CCF advisory committee chairman, felt the kickoff had fulfilled its purpose. "It created the excitement among the leaders. It assisted in sending to those not in attendance the word that the Centennial celebration is a reality, no longer just a dream."

Michael Hulsebus, D.C., another board member exclaimed: "The kickoff was incredible! Too bad it wasn't shared by the entire profession."

Frank Zolli, D.C., dean of the College of Chiropractic, University of Bridgeport, said: "The whole day was just phenomenal. I left the kickoff feeling totally motivated and ready to spread the word about chiropractic and the celebration of our 100th birthday."

**Alan Thicke, David Richards and Dr. Guy Riekeman rehearsing**

**Spine collection proves to be a fine "photo-op."**

# What if they've come to arrest your parents?

One of the most emotional moments of the entire Grand Celebration came at the kickoff luncheon. Keynote speaker Dr. Carl S. Cleveland, III, presented three chiropractic pioneers who lived with the threat (and the reality in two cases) of going to jail for the chiropractic cause. As the pioneers told their stories, more than a few eyes grew moist.

Dr. Cleveland struck an upbeat tone as he related that in his travels he had noticed "two kinds of chiropractors – the torchbearers and the pallbearers. Some people think things are great, and some say things are so bad in their town. Well, things are not bad in your town. Maybe in Haiti or Cuba. But I see great things for chiropractic in any town. I see great things for this profession."

Dr. Cleveland said chiropractic is the golden health care profession and chiropractors will be the wellness practitioners of the 21st century. "The need has never been greater, the opportunity has never been more clear. ... This is our finest hour."

He even cited bad press like *"20/20"* as evidence there is a new awareness about the profession. Chiropractic research, he said, will bring credibility, "credibility brings acceptance, and acceptance brings utilization."

He recounted a boyhood experience involving a nine-year-old neighbor girl named Phyllis, who told him, "My daddy says what your daddy does is bad. My daddy says your daddy is a quack."

Well, Cleveland noted, the children of today's chiropractors won't grow up hearing the word quack

because today the profession is respected. However, even as chiropractic is poised to expand its influence, he said, it's vital that chiropractors appreciate the struggle to get this far, "the struggle for licensure, the struggle to position this profession as a key component of mainstream health care. You need to hear the story of what it's like to hear a knock at the door and be fearful that they've come to arrest your parents."

He introduced his father, Dr. Carl Cleveland, Jr., who recounted that experience as a child growing up in a home that doubled as a chiropractic college in Kansas City. "One thing that was impressed upon me was that, if there was a knock at the door or the ring of the doorbell, my instructions were to stay glued to the spot. I wasn't to move a muscle or let out a peep until my father or mother would go to one side and look out a window. They would discuss who the person was ringing the bell and try to determine if it was a bonafide patient for the clinic or a prospective student or a detective sent to arrest them."

His parents learned to notice the shoes of whoever was at the door. They recognized that detectives were issued a particular kind of comfortable shoe because those were the days before squad cars.

The elder Dr. Cleveland expressed puzzlement his parents never were actually arrested. "If I had been a member of the American Medical Association or the Missouri Medical Association, I would have arrested my father and thrown away the key because he was the one that contacted the patients of the chiropractor who was arrested, made arrangements for them to

*"God has a way of doing things that sets the stage for us in life."*

One of the original Centennial paintings portraying those who went to jail for the profession.

come down to the jailhouse to be adjusted, furnished the portable adjusting table and hired a brass band to play outside the jail."

Next the younger Cleveland introduced the last two chiropractors to go to jail for chiropractic, Drs. B.D. Mooring and E.J. Nosser, both from Louisiana.

Dr. Mooring explained he had decided to become a chiropractor after Dr. Lester Fisher helped him, his son and his wife. He recounted his family's history of serious health problems – a son born spastic, with crossed eyes and suffering from fibril disorders. His wife, too, was sickly, having had several surgeries, "living on hormones, not doing well, then told she would have to have a hysterectomy and both breasts removed. Every penny I could get my hands on went to pay medical bills.

"God has a way of doing things that sets the stage for us in life," he said. A horse-riding accident when he

legislators into doing something, so we just continued to practice."

Both spent time in jail in the 1950s for practicing medicine without a license. The Chiropractic Practice Act wasn't passed in Louisiana until 1974. Ironically, drawn-out court cases resulted in their being arrested shortly after the governor of the state signed the licensing act into law.

Dr. Cleveland had arranged for the two doctors to return to the jail for photographs for the *Illustrated History* book, which they did. In the photo with them is the deputy who was on duty when they were arrested. He was still Dr. Nosser's patient, as was his wife. Dr. Nosser brought hearty laughter when he quipped, "My patients never die."

Noting that the three pioneers represented eight decades of the chiropractic struggle, Dr. Cleveland quoted the words, "Where there's no vision the people

Dr. Carl Cleveland, Jr.

Dr. B.D. Mooring

Dr. E.J. Nosser

was 12 and later a diving accident left him in severe back pain. His friends "took pity" on him and forced him to make an appointment to see the chiropractor. Dr. Fisher gave him an adjustment, and the pain went away almost immediately, not only from the diving accident but from the earlier accident as well. "It was the greatest thing that ever happened."

Then the doctor helped his son. "His eyes straightened immediately. He never had another fibril disorder. Ninety days later we took his braces off, and he got better and better and better. My wife didn't have to have her breasts removed, and I thought, I want to be able to do for other people what this man has done for us." So he enrolled in the Palmer School of Chiropractic.

Dr. Nosser recounted his brushes with the law, brought because he had "probably the first chiropractic sign out in the open so they didn't have any trouble finding me." He said he "wasn't hankering to go to jail, but I knew that the only way to get where we were going was to get some sort of publicity, to shame the

perish," then added: "Where there *is* vision the people prosper." He cited a Chinese proverb: "If you want a year of prosperity, grow grain. If you want 10 years of prosperity, grow a tree. If you want 100 years of prosperity, contribute to the growth of people." The application? Chiropractic's greater contribution is beyond symptomatic care and the treatment of back pain.

He called on the assembled chiropractors to set goals of increasing chiropractic patients from 15 million to 50 million by the year 2,000 and increasing the countries where chiropractic is practiced from 20 to 50 by the year 2,000. "Go home and energize your constituencies, dig deep in your pockets. ... Never take this profession for granted."

Cleveland said that, if he could ever locate his childhood taunter, Phyllis, he would "give her a big hug and thank her for lighting the fire in my belly to fight to position us as a first-class clinical science, to bring our image in line with the reality of today's chiropractic."

With reference to the pioneers, Cleveland concluded, "They have passed the torch to us, and it is our responsibility to sustain that flame."

# Dressed up like D.D., welcomed like Santa

Another CCF idea was to hire an actor to play Daniel David Palmer, the founder of chiropractic. It was hoped appearances by D.D. would add fun and warmth and provide continuity to all the Centennial events. The idea worked.

For veteran West Coast actor David Richards, playing D.D. Palmer throughout the Centennial events was a "dream role." His appearances, which took him around the country, numbered about a dozen including those at chiropractic colleges. "I visited a lot of nice cities, stayed in some great hotels and met a lot of truly wonderful people," Richards said.

Vern Gielow. He concluded that the founder of chiropractic was a man of great warmth and magnetism. "I know he had a combative side to his nature – with his son, B.J., for instance – but for the purposes of my Centennial appearances I saw no reason to bring that in."

He also researched chiropractic and occasionally made substantive comments in the middle of his shtick. One example: "More and more people are turning to alternative forms of health care, and chiropractic is right in the forefront of that."

*"It's still amazing to me how everybody loved that character."*

**Transforming actor David Richards into D.D. Palmer was a time-consuming and tedious task**

He and other actors auditioned for the part about a year and a half before the first Centennial gala, and he made his first appearance as D.D. in a promotional video produced for the profession. "I had developed an interest in playing historical characters and had done F.D.R. in *Annie,* but, to tell you the truth, I had no idea what I was getting into with D.D. Palmer. I never would have guessed I'd have so much fun playing somebody 150 years old."

The actor actually had a long list of impressive acting credits. Television appearances included "The Bold & the Beautiful," "The Young & the Restless," "Perry Mason," "The Young Riders," "Father Dowling," "One Day at a Time" and "The Facts of Life." His 63 theater productions included "Guys and Dolls," "Harvey," "The Taming of the Shrew," "Last of the Red Hot Lovers," "Best Little Whorehouse in Texas," "Barefoot in the Park," "Once Upon a Mattress," "On Golden Pond," "Zorba," "Mame" and "The Sound of Music." He also has more than 120 radio and television commercials to his credit.

Richards said his research of D.D.'s character included reading *Old Dad Chiro*, the Palmer biography by

In the letter he wrote accepting the job, Richards noted: "I'm a committed believer in, and grateful recipient of, the art of chiropractic, and it is heart-warming to spend extended time with a body of healers whose healing is based on touch and communication."

His clothing was authentic 19th century, down to the size nine boots. He and his makeup artist, Sue Cary Mayer, studied photographs of D.D. and pinned them on the wall each time he was made up, a tedious undertaking that required two and a half hours. Hair for D.D.'s bushy eyebrows was cut and attached each time.

Richards was especially proud of the beard, which was originally created by a technician at the Chicago Opera. "The beard was a blend of seven colors of human hair and some yak hair. Human hair tends to turn green, and the yak hair helps preserve the original color. It was all hand-tied to a net and shaped to my face. One of the great compliments to Sue was that several times people would be up very close and, in all seriousness, ask me how long it took me to grow it."

Richards' portrayal of the character highlighted a grandfatherly kindness and wit that may or may not have been the real D.D., but the Richards' version was received like, oh, say, Santa Claus. "It is still amazing to me how everybody loved that character. Everywhere I went I was treated like a star, and then, after I was around for a few minutes, they treated me like an old friend."

David Anderson, D.C., who assisted Dr. Holmberg with hundreds of Centennial details, said that he was most impressed with the actor's ability to react like D.D. in a variety of situations. "He never came out of the part, so after a few minutes you would start to look at him as though he really was D.D. Palmer."

Dr. William Holmberg agreed. "D.D. – I mean, David – really knows how to think on his feet. There were situations we didn't have time to script, and he'd just wing it. He always had something witty or nostalgic or meaningful to say, even ad libbing. The guy's a pro."

At an early session of the Centennial kickoff, before Dr. William Holmberg let the actor playing D.D. Palmer take over the podium, he cracked perhaps the first of the year's many lame chiropractic jokes:

"After D.D. adjusted Harvey Lillard, Harvey got up from the table, and said, "Thank you, thank you, I can hear.' Then he asked D.D. how much he owed for the office visit. When D.D. said $50, Harvey said, 'Huh?'"

# Kickoff news release sets aggressive tone

Although the public relations agencies had a variety of good ideas implemented to generate Centennial publicity, the aggressive tone that eventually characterized the effort was determined by the CCF planners. It got its start at the kickoff.

Juan Nodarse, who laid out the public relations plans for kickoff attendees, sat through kickoff planning sessions and sensed that previous public relations planning was less than complete. He grabbed his staff writer and ordered up a story, which the agencies in turn distributed. It would set the theme of much of the press coverage.

Its title was, "Chiropractors See Expanding Role in 'Redefined Health Care'" Here are a few paragraphs from that release.

*"What we're seeing is that the present approach to health, which is treating people after they are sick, is neither adequately beneficial nor cost-effective," Dr. (William) Holmberg said. "We need to head off problems before they become too dire to remedy and too costly for either individuals or society to deal with."*

*Guy Riekeman, D.C., a Palmer College graduate and prominent chiropractor from Colorado Springs, Colorado, added that awareness of the need for more emphasis on prevention is growing among many health care professionals and researchers.*

*"Many leading-edge health care thinkers are saying that we have to protect individuals' potential for good health from conception into old age," Dr. Riekeman said.*

*"Chiropractors, with their philosophical emphasis on a healthy lifestyle, are well-positioned to become part of a team of health care professionals working together to maximize every aspect of a healthy and wholesome life.*

*In addition, Dr. Riekeman explained that the recent reports of the public's widespread use of alternative health care and the clamoring for cost-reduction in health care services indicate that a major shift in public thinking has already occurred.*

*"The public has already redefined health care, and now it's up to all of us as health care professionals to catch up," he said.*

With that initial news release, prepared on the spot, chiropractic public relations hit the ground running.

# Chiropractic history? It's in Centennial book

One of the Centennial's most substantial legacies was publication of perhaps the definitive book on the chiropractic profession. *Chiropractic: An Illustrated History* is a massive, 533-page volume with 939 illustrations depicting 100 years of chiropractic memories, accomplishments and growth.

The book was co-authored by Glenda Wiese, CCF board member representing the Association for the History of Chiropractic (AHC), and Dennis

Dennis Peterson                    Glenda Wiese

Peterson, director of the David D. Palmer Health Services Library at Palmer College of Chiropractic.

The project, in association with the AHC and the Chiropractic Centennial Foundation, involved extensive research to obtain photos and artifacts from around the world, many formerly unpublished.

*"It will be an invaluable resource for everybody interested at all in chiropractic. ..."*

"It was a huge undertaking," Peterson said. "Glenda and I feel like we've given birth, and a very large baby it is."

Meticulous attention to detail is given to everything from historic episodes to chiropractic equipment to personalities to professional associations to legislation and professional persecution. The book jacket gives merely a hint of the scope:

*The healing arts, traditions and practices of what today is called Chiropractic have been known and handed down from generation to generation in virtually every culture on earth. "Adjusting" the spine, neck, skull, shoulder, elbow, wrist, hip, knee, ankle, toes and feet for various ailments has been practiced for centuries. The specific modern healing art called Chiropractic began in 1895 in the small Mississippi river town of Davenport, Iowa. Daniel David Palmer, a Canadian immigrant, began the profession and devoted his life to establishing it as a rational science, art and philosophy. The story of his extraordinary life and the lives of those he influenced through the years is told here in pictures and text. There are chapters on technique and radiology, chiropractic around the world, equipment, women in chiropractic, controversies within the profession, chiropractic education and much more. The final chapter is an epilogue on the future of chiropractic in the twenty-first century. A selected bibliography and exhaustive index add to the value of this superb volume.*

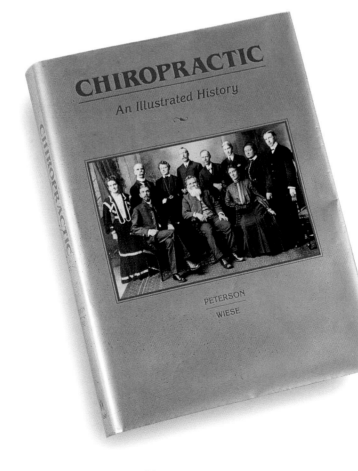

**Publishing *Chiropractic: An Illustrated History* was a major accomplishment of the Centennial Foundation**

Contributing writers, along with Peterson and Wiese, include prominent names in the profession, especially chiropractic historians: Stanley Bolton, D.C., Alana Callender, M.S.L.S., Robin Canterbury, D.C., Mary-Anne Chance, D.C., Carl S. Cleveland, III, D.C., Meridel Gatterman, D.C., Pierre Louis Gaucher-Peslherbe, D.C., Ph.D., Russell Gibbons, Joseph C. Keating, Jr., Ph.D., John S. Kyneur, D.C., Herb Lee, D.C., F.I.C.C., George McAndrews, J.D., Jerome F. McAndrews, D.C., Rolf Peters, B.Sc., D.C., William S. Rehm, D.C., William G. Rothstein, Herbert J. Vear, D.C., F.C.C.S., LL.D., and Walter I. Wardwell, Ph.D.

"This is simply a fantastic book and a Herculean accomplishment," said Dr. William Holmberg, CCF president. "It will be an invaluable resource for everybody interested at all in chiropractic and the healing arts."

The book, which sells for $84.95, may be ordered from Mosby, Inc., 1-800-426-4545. Mention code #07735 for *Chiropractic: An Illustrated History* when ordering.

## "Passing the Torch"

The CCF produced a series of limited edition *Passing the Torch* commemorative audio tapes, with speeches by such chiropractic pioneers as Dr. B.J. Palmer, Dr. Galen Price, Dr. Clarence Gonstead, Dr. Carl Cleveland, Sr., Dr. Carl Cleveland, Jr., and others. Contemporary speakers included Dr. Fred Barge, Dr. Carl S. Cleveland, III, Dr. Russell Erhardt, Dr. Reginald Gold, Dr. Jerry McAndrews, Dr. James Parker, Dr. Guy Riekeman, Dr. Louis Sportelli, Dr. Virgil Strang and Dr. Sid Williams.

Each set of 16 audio cassettes was presented in a gold leaf embossed stamp case and sold for $250. Proceeds went toward the campaign for national media exposure.

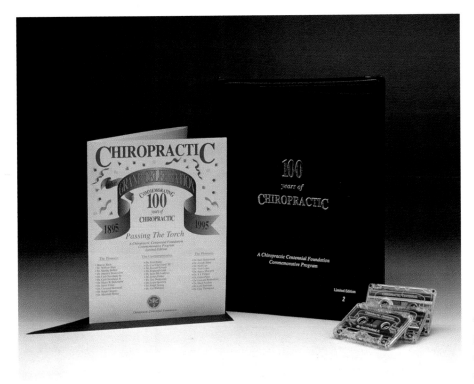

**Chiropractic history, philosophy and life experiences were captured on audio tape**

# Witch doctor's look "would melt a crowbar," J. Clay recalls

As one method of telling the story of the first 100 years of chiropractic, the CCF worked with the Oral History Program at California State University in Fullerton to produce tape recordings of 40 histories. A selection of them was transcribed into a volume entitled *Chiropractic Pioneers: A Remembrance.*

Listening to the tapes or reading the transcriptions fulfills the wish stated in the volume's preface: "It is the Chiropractic Centennial Foundation's wish that the colorful and sometimes poignant memories shared in this volume will help capture the sense of drama and struggle that has been chiropractic's crucible during its first hundred years."

The tapes are rich in anecdotes that convey the flavor of the beliefs and practices of the chiropractic pioneers. Here's one from Dr. J. Clay Thompson, who recounted his exciting experience in an Amazon village.

On the way to the village, Dr. Thompson, two medical doctors, two contractors and a sports writer passed several shrunken heads "hanging all around

Dr. J. Clay Thompson

on little strings." Their tour guide informed them that the chief was very sick.

*We walked about a hundred yards into a clearing, and the chief was sitting on a log, and he was going, "Ooh! Ooh!" I could see he was sick. He was the head of the camp, and it was really something [to see]. A witch doctor was all painted up, and he was shaking bird wings in one hand and bats in the other. He didn't look very favorably toward us. He gave me a look that would have melted a two-inch crowbar. It really scared the hell out of me. We were standing there, and all of a sudden one of them said something to the chief. The chief looked around, said something back, and then said something to the interpreter. She said to me, "The chief wants you to do something. I'd not refuse him, if I were you." How do you like that? Down there you don't have a colonic irrigator, a Thompson table, or an x-ray, no electricity, not a damn thing but your hands and God. I went over and palpated his neck, and the axis was practically sticking out the side of his neck. I thought, I'd better get it [the first] time. I took an old hold on [his neck], an old osteopathic hold. You could hear it move in the next camp. His eyes went this way, he went that way, and I thought, God, I've had it. Pretty soon he said something to the interpreter. He said, "Headache gone. Belly feels better."*

*Of course, I quit while I was ahead. You're damn right. I said, "Let's get out of here." You should have seen the M.D.s! Their hair was sticking straight up, because if they'd have been asked to do this job. ... I thought to myself, what a comparison! No black bag, nothing but my hands. Just the knowledge that his Innate's the same size as mine. ...*

Others who contributed their oral histories, as preserved in the volume, included Dr. Herbert Vear, past president of Canadian Memorial Chiropractic College and Western States Chiropractic College; Vern Gielow, administrative assistant to Dr. David Palmer; Dr. Earl Homewood, past president of Canadian Memorial Chiropractic College and dean at other colleges; Carl Cleveland, Jr., chancellor of Cleveland Chiropractic Colleges; and Dr. Dan Spears, administrator at the Spears Chiropractic Hospital.

In a sad footnote to the project, both Dr. Thompson and Dr. Cleveland, Jr., passed away during the Centennial year.

# The kickoff message: Hold hands, stick together

The evening program at Davenport's Adler Theatre was a smash ending to the Centennial kickoff and an emotional highlight of the entire year. A bright pastiche of humor, reflection and inspiration, the program carried its audience of a thousand or so from saluting the courageous pioneers of the past to focusing on a promising future.

After a video introduction, an off-stage announcer thrilled the audience: "Welcome ladies and gentlemen to the Chiropractic Centennial Kickoff – a project in the making for 10 years and in the hearts and souls of the profession for almost 100 years."

On came Dr. Gary Street, representing the ICA, and Dr. Russell Sawyer, representing the ACA. Their messages were reinforced in a broader context by Dr. Christoph Diem of Switzerland, representing the World Federation of Chiropractic. He noted that the organization now represents more than 60 nations worldwide. He ended with a stirring plea for unity, a theme repeated throughout the evening. "It is my personal wish that we do not use this next year – or the next 100 years maybe – with infighting and divisiveness. United we stand is our only chance to counter the pressures that will continue to come upon our profession."

Next came greetings from various chiropractic leaders and supporters, including one from Vice President Al Gore. Then comedian Alan Thicke walked out on stage to a rousing welcome.

His opening segued from the near impossibility of traveling from Vancouver, British Columbia, to Moline, Illinois, to an apology to the chiropractic profession. Years earlier he read a joke on his hit television show "Growing Pains" that was unflattering about chiropractic. Since his sister is a chiropractor, he heard about his *faux pas* from her and many others. "Boy, did I hear about it!" His sister, he said, made sure he received "an attitude adjustment."

The light came up on D.D. Palmer adjusting a patient toward the back of the stage. Thicke cracked another joke at D.D.'s expense. When D.D. corrected Harvey Lillard's hearing, he heard his wife for the first time in 17 years, Thicke quipped, "and, D.D., he never forgave you for that."

Thicke introduced D.D. to his great-granddaughter, Vickie Palmer, in the front row, then brought in Dr. Carl Cleveland, Jr., and Dr. Galen Price. They and D.D. handled the next segment, reviewing the great advances of early chiropractic history.

The lights went down, and the announcer read a quote from B.J. Palmer:

*"Today we stand on the threshold of our great responsibility to save what we have. As years have crept upon us, we find that we have exhausted ourselves. We have now come to the point where we are passing this great responsibility upon you younger men and women. You have a lifetime ahead of you. Our life is beginning to recede. We are passing this challenge to you, now, today, to save what we have labored so long, so diligently to protect, preserve and survive for the sake of humankind."*

**Alan Thicke's monologue was a big hit**

The lights came up on Dr. Guy Riekeman and a little boy, Casey Mohr, there to represent future generations of chiropractors. Although it wasn't intended, Casey brought more laughter from the crowd, waving to his daddy off stage and yawning during Riekeman's presentation. But the good doctor persevered, calling on the audience to imagine that "there were no coincidences," that they as chiropractors were there at the right moment in history to lead a revolution in health care. Then a video with music and graphics asked the audience to imagine that new world.

Dr. Riekeman followed with a reference to the book *All I Really Need to Know I Learned in Kindergarten.* "Hold hands and stick together" was the line Riekeman used to exhort the profession to unity.

After still another moving video segment, the program came to a big finish as its participants appeared on stage to throw confetti and respond to a standing ovation. With the Pointer Sisters' "I'm So Excited" rocking in the background, the happy crowd continued their rhythmic clapping for several minutes. At one point Alan Thicke shouted, "Let the Celebration Begin!"

It already had.

*"Today we stand on the threshold of our great responsibility to save what we have."*

The make-believe D.D. Palmer and the real D.D.'s great-granddaughter, Vickie A. Palmer, Chairman of the Board of Trustees, Palmer Chiropractic University System

# Hey, that's your cue!

One of the most high pressure jobs in Centennial planning involved retaining and riding herd on the entertainment for the various Centennial events. The job fell to Mary Rowe, who acted as entertainment coordinator and stage manager, assisting Dr. Jerilynn Kaibel, who had overall responsibility.

Imagine putting on full-blown stage productions, including the kickoff evening program and the entertainment at Washington and Davenport, involving many amateur entertainers, people who don't show up on time or who are unfamiliar with the scripts, who are nervous and distracted – it can keep you up nights.

Mary Rowe saw to it that people got on stage when they were supposed to and pretty much mother-henned the three entertainment programs on the fly. She was one of hundreds of people who helped make the celebration grand.

Dr. Jerilynn Kaibel and Mary Rowe helped keep the entertainment on track

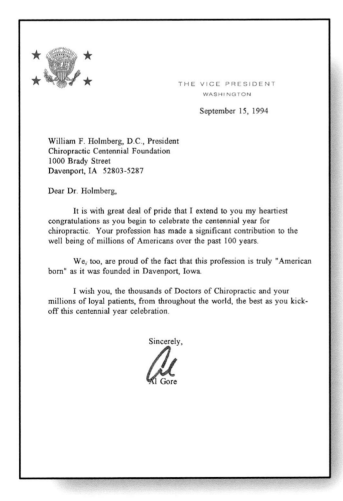

Vice President Al Gore sent congratulations to the chiropractic profession

The kickoff program had a rousing finish

35

# Centennial Year Begins with a Parade

*There was nervous energy aplenty among the Centennial planners as they staked their reputations and donor money on a chiropractic float in the Rose Parade. Would it garner the media attention the profession deserved? An elaborate New Year's Eve party got everybody fired up, and then they waited for their float to roll into view.*

## How the Rose Parade float idea took flight

*"We knew it was a good association between chiropractic... and the quest for excellence."*

Donald M. Petersen, Jr., the editor of *Dynamic Chiropractic*, and Michael Schroeder, Esq., general counsel for the California Chiropractic Association, were flying together on a project in 1986 when they noticed an article about the Rose Parade in an in-flight magazine. The article said the Rose Parade is the second most-watched event in the world, next to the World Cup soccer tournament.

"Wouldn't it be great," Schroeder recalled saying, "if we could have a chiropractic float in the Rose Parade?" And that's what they decided to do.

They planned to form a non-profit corporation to raise money for the float, with no thought of any other profession-wide Centennial plans. In fact, they submitted their plan to the Tournament of Roses committee six years before the event and received initial approval and a formal application. The idea, born on an airplane, had taken flight.

The Rose Parade float idea had surfaced from other quarters. CCF records contain a letter of May 30, 1991, saying the board had rejected the idea from another party. But with Petersen and Schroeder already rolling, the CCF took another look. All agreed that whatever was done should be integrated into the overall Centennial planning. So, Petersen and Schroeder came aboard as part of the planning team, Petersen as a trustee and Schroeder as chairman of the special projects committee.

The theme of the chiropractic float

"We merged with the CCF to create a fund-raising synergy," Schroeder said. "Rick Flaherty of Leander Health Technologies put together the CCF fund-raising package, and we were able to use Rose Parade and Rose Bowl tickets and seating as a key part of the benefits package for the major donors."

Before the Rose Parade came the
New Year's Eve party for the pro-
fession's leaders like Dr. Marilyn
Smith and Dr. Russell Erhardt

Schroeder and Petersen also played roles in determining what the float looked like. They interviewed several float designers before deciding on Estes Parade Floats, one of the most experienced and a frequent prize-winner. "We knew it was a good association between chiropractic and the parade theme about sports and the quest for excellence," Schroeder said. "We went back and forth with several concepts – I think we saw 20 different drawings – before coming up with the eagle and the athletes around it."

Schroeder, Flaherty and Petersen were among the volunteers who worked on the float, helping glue flowers in place and making sure everything was as it should be up to the start of the Parade.

Who would ride the float? Chiropractors recommended others in the profession. A couple of the major donors wondered if they could ride, but the CCF planners had a better idea. They went after top-name athletes who had benefited from chiropractic.

Schroeder wrote for help to Jan Corwin, D.C., and Jack Barnatham, D.C., presidents of the ACA and ICA Sports Councils respectively: "The themes that we want to convey to the float audience about chiropractic are excellence and the future. We therefore are interested in having athletes who are either professional or amateur who are recognized as the best in their field of endeavor... and in all cases it would mean athletes who are recognized role models."

Those ultimately selected as float riders were professional baseball great Joe Morgan, Olympic gold medalist skater Cathy Turner and golf prodigy Tiger Woods.

Getting country music singer Lee Greenwood was another story.

"I really wanted Lee Greenwood, but nobody seemed to have any connection with him," Schroeder recalled, "so I just called him up. I told him that unless he was planning to play in the World Cup he would never get more exposure than on the chiropractic float." The rest, as they say, is history.

Looking back, Schroeder said the Rose Parade and all that went with it "was amazing. The hassle of finding lodging and transportation for 350 people, of lining up limos for the celebrities, of getting passes for people to get through police lines and all the rest was a nightmare. We had a staff of 20 volunteers working for six months. Still, when it was over, I'd have to say it was gratifying.

"That little article on the airplane turned into a major positive experience in my life."

A chiropractic float was Michael Schroeder's dream

# Chiropractic float is mechanical wonder

The chiropractic float, like the others in the Rose Parade, proved to be not only a thing of beauty but a marvel of engineering.

It had to be to support 50,000 pounds on the move. The float was 55 feet tall and 18 feet long. The huge eagle centerpiece would rotate as would six spiraling rays of stars. Toward the end of the parade route, the head and 40-foot wings had to be dropped to go beneath a viaduct with an 18-foot clearance, then come back up to full height.

The vehicle to carry that bulk had power steering, an automatic transmission and a rebuilt, big block Ford V-8 engine. Two people would operate it, an operator driving blind and an "observer" looking through a small peep hole and communicating via intercom. The tires were foam-filled so no nail would stop the float. Yet it was the engineering above the chassis and drive train that would determine the float's success.

The mastermind behind the chiropractic float was Tim Estes, president of Fiesta Parade Floats and a well-known name in the float-building industry, having 20 years of experience, 200 Rose Parade floats and scores of parade prizes under his belt.

In interviews with *Dynamic Chiropractic*, Estes described the progress of the float construction and gave a good idea of some of its engineering challenges.

"The float overall has six tires and four casters, so there are actually 10 points touching the ground, and all the weight is distributed over the 55-foot length of the float. The four casters, two at each end of the float, each handle 10,000 pounds. The steering axle can handle 16,000 pounds and the drive axle can handle 24,000 pounds," Estes said.

The superstructure, built of heavy steel, would also distribute the huge weight and accommodate the eagle's rotation.

"Right in the center of the float is an 11-foot diameter ring that is eight-inch beam steel that's been bent

**Driving blind, with tons of stuff overhead**

and rolled. That's what the eagle rotates on. In the center of it, it has a 40,000-pound capacity thrust bearing holding the majority of the weight, and then we have eight stabilizing wheels – each with a capacity of 2,000 pounds – around the perimeter."

Aluminum and pencil steel were used to shape the rest of the float, which was then covered with aluminum window screen. Next the float was sprayed with a thick, weblike latex material called cocooning.

"That allows us to go ahead and paint the areas. Technically, when a float is decorated correctly, you'll never see the paint, but people decorate by the colors of the paint. In case a flower falls off, then you have the paint there to make it all mesh together."

Throughout the months-long building process parade officials and mechanics would inspect the float in various stages. Ultimately they would check 315 "inspection points," and all those aspects would have to pass inspection before the float was approved.

More went into the chiropractic float than met the eye.

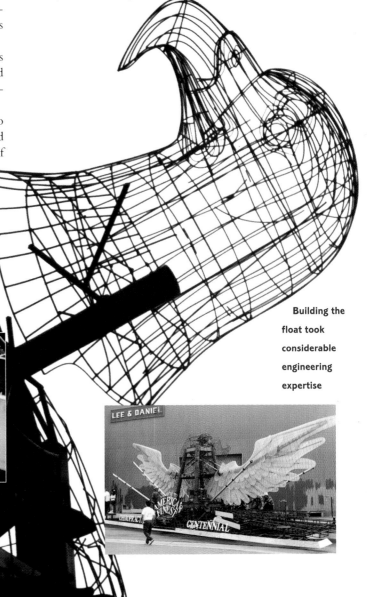

**Building the float took considerable engineering expertise**

## Lee Greenwood song lifts the crowd

Country music great Lee Greenwood, who thrilled Rose Parade spectators singing his hit "God Bless the USA," is a great American success story. From his humble beginnings on a California farm, his determination and talents led him to country music stardom.

Having won two consecutive titles as the Country Music Association's "Male Vocalist of the Year," Greenwood's career already was in high gear when he won the CMA "Song of the Year" honors for writing "God Bless the USA." The patriotic song has since been performed repeatedly across the country and found a niche in the national culture. During the Persian Gulf War, it was reportedly the favorite song of General Norman Schwarzkopf. *Country Music* magazine lists it among its top 100 country music songs of all time.

"Chiropractic has been helpful to me throughout my career," Greenwood said. "I acquired a back injury long ago in a softball game, and playing the keyboards occasionally would aggravate it. It was those times when I found relief in chiropractic."

Greenwood's performing the patriotic song on the chiropractic float strengthened the association between chiropractic and good things about America. Like the singer, the chiropractic profession started from simple beginnings in a country where determination and ability pay off.

## Joe Morgan gives chiropractic credit

Joe Morgan, just about all-everything in professional baseball, said he still depends on his chiropractor, Dr. Jan Corwin, to keep him fit a decade after his retirement.

Morgan is one of a handful of players chosen for the Hall of Fame (in 1990) in their first year of eligibility, joining the elite company of first-timers like Jackie Robinson, Bob Feller, Stan Musial, Sandy Koufax, Mickey Mantle, Willie Mays and Hank Aaron.

Morgan began his career in 1964 with the Houston Astros where he was named "Rookie of the Year." He played with the Astros until 1972 when he was traded to the Cincinnati Reds, where he was named "Most Valuable Player" in the All-Star Game. He was the "Most Valuable Player" in the National League in 1975 and 1976 and received the "Commissioner's Award" in 1976 for the most votes from fans for the All-Star Game.

He was "Comeback Player of the Year" in 1982. Throughout his career he won five "Golden Gloves," played in 10 All-Star Games and recorded 689 stolen bases.

"Early in my career it was fairly easy to recover from minor injuries," Morgan said. "However, as I got older, I wasn't able to bounce back from injuries quite as easily, and I realized that I needed assistance keeping my body properly aligned. ... Although I no longer play professional baseball, I'm still active in sports. Whether golfing, playing tennis or skiing, without the benefits of chiropractic, I don't think I would be able to remain as fit and active today."

## Golf phenom lives up to his expectations

The chiropractic profession scored a big Tournament of Roses coup when it landed Eldrick "Tiger" Woods to ride the chiropractic float. The youngest winner of the U.S. Amateur golf tournament in its 99-year history, Tiger Woods is a legend in the making.

Like the chiropractic profession itself, he has great expectations. When he was 11, he constructed a chart to mount over his bed showing when Jack Nicklaus won the major golf tournaments. "I wanted to be the youngest player ever to win the majors," Woods said.

When he became the first African-American to win the United States Amateur in 1994, he did it at the age of 18 years eight months, one month earlier than young Jack Nicklaus won his.

As a baby, he dragged around a sawed-off putter instead of a rattle, and at 10 months began hitting golf balls in the family's garage. He was the youngest ever to play in a PGA tournament in the United States when he teed off in the Los Angeles Open at 16. He won the U.S. Junior in 1991, 1992 and 1993 before going on to win his first U.S. Amateur.

His win there came with a classic six-shot, final-round rally highlighted by a twisting, 15-foot birdie putt on the 17th hole – the greatest comeback ever at the Amateur.

The golf phenom is an unabashed chiropractic booster. "Being a chiropractic patient has really helped me a lot. When I was in a growth spurt, my back became very sore, and I was weak," Woods said. (My chiropractor) not only adjusted my spine, but he also gave me strengthening exercises to do. If you are tall and gangly, like I am, or play sports, I would recommend chiropractic."

Eight months after the Tournament of Roses Parade, Tiger Woods, 19, a friend of chiropractic, won his second U.S. Amateur tournament. The legend continues.

## Olympian owes much to chiropractic

Cathy Turner, a two-time Olympic gold medalist and the chiropractic float's lone female rider, is a gutsy performer who won gold medals in two consecutive Winter Olympic Games. In Albertville, France, in 1992, she won the women's 500-meter short track competition and also took home a silver medal. In Lillehammer, Norway, Cathy won a gold and a bronze.

She credits chiropractic with helping her success: "After retiring for nine years, I decided to make my comeback into speed skating. I began with an aggressive workout program. During a squat exercise, lifting 286 pounds, a spotter picked me up the wrong way. That resulted in a separation of my vertebrae," she recalled. "I sought a chiropractor in my home town. For quite a while, chiropractic care was mandatory for my training program."

Cathy Turner's float appearance along with that of the other athletes, standing proudly amid cascading floral bouquets as patients and advocates of chiropractic, prompted NBC commentator Joe Garagiola to exclaim, "They've really got some champions on that float!

For the chiropractors
at the Rose Parade,
their float's coming
into view was an
unforgettable moment

Photograph by
Charles Allen

# Flowers, like chiropractic – salute to the natural

One aspect that made the Rose Parade a fitting venue for chiropractic is its commitment to flowers, the exquisite expression of beauty and fragility in nature. The parade is to flowers what chiropractic is to non-invasive procedures. They both speak of respect, even reverence, for what is *natural*.

Rose Parade policy insists that every feature of a float except the tires be covered with flowers, nuts, berries, fronds or other vegetation. For the chiropractic float and its majestic eagle, the flowers, coconut chips, rice and foliage would total approximately seven tons. In fact, the combined weight of all the flowers and water-filled plastic vials to keep them alive equaled the weight of the float's steel structure.

Of course, it is not the number of flowers but their arrangement that counts. The goal for the floral design of the chiropractic float was to create "one of those really heart-throbbing floats," according to Jim Hynd, vice president and floral director of Fiesta Parade Floats and a charter member of the American Institute of Floral Designers.

The chiropractic float was decorated with 10 varieties of flowers, many imported from distant corners of the world, including forsythia, a yellow blossom from Europe, and the Oncidum orchid, a small flower grown in Singapore. The float also used such home-grown natural elements as corn husks and eucalyptus foliage.

The main flower for the eagle's body and wings was a tawny gold chrysanthemum, fading into a cream-colored chrysanthemum, and a white chrysanthemum at the very edge of the wings. The head and neck "feathers" were of white coconut chips from the Philippines. Hynd described the flower arrangement at the base of the eagle as an "explosion" of imported white and yellow forsythias.

Radiating lines of flowers decorated the front and rear of the float. The lower section was red Gerber daisies and orange-red roses. The higher elevations were lighter oranges and hot pinks, culminating in champagne-colored Oceania roses.

The perimeter garden inside the framework along either side was of large purple orchids and a profusion of red – Gerbers, carnations, and large Dallas roses in the center. The radiating stars and rod work were covered in white rice, then augmented by blossoms of the Oncidium and Dendrovium orchids, and tiny white-button pom-pons atop the rays.

Flowers, flowers everywhere

The entire framework around the deck was deep purple Dendrovium orchids called "Madame Pompadour" and edged with crisp, white button chrysanthemums.

Mounting and preserving all those flowers was no small trick. Attaching the flowers and foliage required seven types of glue. The float carried on its underbelly 100,000 plastic water vials to keep the flowers alive.

The chiropractors and their families who saw the float stood in awe. Perhaps Dr. Marilyn Smith, a practitioner in Coronado, California, and a CCF trustee, described it most eloquently the day before the parade:

"When I see this golden eagle and all these beautiful flowers and when I think about the noble mission of our profession that it all represents, I think this float will be a fitting symbol for us long after the parade is over and the flowers are gone. I know I'll hold this spectacular image as long as I live."

# Glue-fingered chiropractors help out

Decorating the chiropractic float was a huge, tedious task. It took many hands, and those of area chiropractors, their spouses and children were among them. A delegation came over from the San Diego Chiropractic Society and worked long and hard on the project. Even members of the CCF board and their families did their bit in stuffing flowers into plastic vials and gluing on flowers and other materials.

It all took place in a huge tent and warehouse facility of Fiesta Floats, which becomes a giant greenhouse each year for the Rose Parade.

"Everybody have something to do? Everybody know what they're doing?" A decorating supervisor asked that again and again three days before the parade as scores of glue-fingered volunteers worked away. Fiesta Floats employees in red jackets or T-shirts moved throughout the grounds, answering questions and inspecting the progress. Tim Estes, a huge man with a red beard, who is the president of Fiesta Floats, talked frequently on his walkie-talkie. Boxes of flowers were stacked everywhere, and a sweet flower smell hung in the air.

It was an intense time, a day in what float regulars call Hell Week, but there were plenty of smiles, wisecracks and horseplay as well. The old, young and in-between worked happily side by side.

The industriousness of the volunteers, including many who had no particular interest in chiropractic, was remarkable. Many worked for several days on the project. A girl named Devin, a 12-year-old from nearby Rialto, California, said she was working on the chiropractic float because she liked flowers and the excitement of the Parade.

"I just like to see it get done," she said. "I just like to stand there at the Parade and say, 'I worked on that float' when it goes by."

For her and many others, the chiropractic float was a source of community pride.

Mrs. Donald (Evelyn) Petersen, Jr., helps out decorating the float

## "Monumental task, moment"

Pamela Bear, a seventh trimester student at New York Chiropractic College, wrote about her experience as a float decorator. Walking into the tent in Azuza, California, where the chiropractic float and seven others were being constructed, Pamela reported:

*"You can't imagine the detail that goes into a project of this size. Rick Flaherty of Leander Health Technologies and his wife were busy gluing corn flowers, one at a time, onto the wings of the eagle. The Flahertys had donated considerable time and money to the project. Another D.C. and his family came from Ohio to participate in the building of the float and spent one full day shredding coconut in preparation for this day's gluing onto the sprays that shot out from below the eagle. Dr. Michael Villaverde and his wife, Cindy, of Chino, glued paper-thin luneria petals onto the frame of the float. ...*

*"Monday was the big day. I watched the float roll down the road past the cameras and was in awe – this beautiful float was created for the chiropractic profession. Everyone that had worked so hard and spent so many hours had completed their task, and there was the result on national television for everyone to see. A monumental task for a profession that is celebrating a monumental moment – our Centennial."*

# Rose Parade people are pro-chiropractic

The enthusiasm of CCF representatives and the float's significance to the profession weren't lost on many associated with the Rose Parade.

In accepting the chiropractic float entry, Pasadena Tournament of Roses President Michael E. Ward, said: "In inviting (the) Chiropractic Centennial (Foundation) to participate in the Tournament of Roses, we recognize the important contributions the chiropractic profession makes in improving individuals' health and well being."

Commenting on the acceptance of the chiropractic entry, Michael Schroeder, chairman of the CCF's special projects committee, noted: "I'm elated not only by this invitation but also by the Tournament of Roses' clear recognition of the importance of the chiropractic profession. ..."

Many voiced support for chiropractic and displayed understanding of the issues facing the profession. Consider this perceptive comment from the 17-year-old Rose Parade Queen, Aliya Haque: "Personally, for me, health care reform is a very big issue. ... I think what could happen in a national system is, for example, if I had a car accident and wanted to see a chiropractor, it might not be covered under the national health plan, and I might have to go to a doctor who would want me to have surgery. So, I think, for me, having the open choice that is available now in the private sector is better than having the government dictate to me who is best to treat me."

# New Year's Eve party – first class all the way

The main reason the CCF board went to California at the beginning of the Centennial year was to see the chiropractic float in the Rose Parade, but before the parade was the party. It was touted as "the New Year's Eve party of a lifetime," and, for the scores of chiropractors and families who attended, that's what it was.

Michael Schroeder, Esq., who planned the event, said the objective was to start off the Centennial year with a "classy celebration" and send a signal that the profession is proud and prospering. Everything about the party – location, menu and entertainment – met that criteria.

The party was held at the elegant Regent Beverly Wilshire Hotel in Beverly Hills, California. The hotel fronts on famous Rodeo Drive, and its inside decor with elegant wallcoverings, furnishings and crystal chandeliers is equally posh.

Dr. Jerilynn S. Kaibel summed up the party like this: "Everything about the New Year's Eve party was first class – location, food, entertainment, attendees – just like chiropractic should always be – FIRST CLASS!"

Spirits were high as the evening began with cocktails and hors d'oeuvres, and they just kept rising. The talk was all about the profession's putting aside differences to work for a promising future.

The Bob Gale orchestra brought high-powered musical excitement to the party, and, if any were reluctant to get out on the dance floor, a troupe of professional dancers went out into the crowd and dragged them to their feet.

There were the leaders of the chiropractic profession, many with strong philosophical differences, dancing with their spouses, all together in the conga lines. There was dignified Dr. Kerwin Winkler, the ACA's representative on the CCF, jitterbugging with a young blond dancer in bobby socks and a poodle skirt.

**Dr. William Holmberg and his wife, Barbara**

*"... the pure elation I felt when the curtain dropped and everyone came into the grand ballroom."*

**Some people, like Dr. Jacques A. Fourie, in hat, know how to stand out in a crowd**

**Dr. Kerwin Winkler wasn't afraid to cut loose on the dance floor**

The special lighting effects, including a laser light show playing across the room with the huge Centennial banner as a backdrop, added drama to the affair. The chatter about the Centennial and the midnight toast rallied the guests to the chiropractic cause.

"What I remember most about the New Year's Eve party," Schroeder recalled, "was the pure elation I felt when the curtain dropped and everyone came into the grand ballroom. As the guests were walking in, the band started with a very high energy piece of music as the laser light show cut in. The lasers radiated out over the guests' heads and through the fog that came down from the ceiling. It was one heck of an opening for a New Year's Eve party!"

For Dr. Carl S. Cleveland, III, though, memories are bittersweet. He spent the time with his father, Dr. Carl S. Cleveland, Jr. "It turned out to be the last New Year's Eve that my family and I will spend with him." The senior Dr. Cleveland, one of the profession's elder statesmen, passed away not long after.

Trustee Glenda Wiese remembers "the poshness of the Beverly Wilshire Hotel and the number of courses and wines. ... After a midnight toast with those at our table my husband and I took a quiet stroll along Rodeo Drive. Quite a change of pace for an Iowa farm girl!"

It was, all in all, a thrilling beginning to the profession's most important year. On the bus trip back to the hotels in Pasadena, Dr. William Holmberg led the chiropractors in a ribald sing-along. "The mood was very cheerful – to put it mildly," he said.

Dr. Carl Cleveland, Jr.
and Dr. and Mrs. Carl
S. Cleveland, III

Fun, fun, fun...

Dr. Louis Latimer's
gesture said it all

Conga lines
were a big hit

Rick and Cathy Flaherty

After all, it was
New Year's Eve

# A moment of truth at the 210 Freeway

Dr. William Holmberg had misgivings about the Rose Parade float. No, make that a nightmare.

Beyond concerns about the cost and the true extent of media exposure, Holmberg was worried that "the damn thing won't work." The giant eagle was to rotate 180 degrees. More significantly, both the head and the wings had to be lowered to pass under the Interstate 210 viaduct over the parade route, which swings north off Colorado Boulevard onto Sierra Madre Boulevard to San Gabriel Boulevard.

The 210 bridge has a clearance of 18 feet. The eagle was 55-feet tall. The head and the 40-foot

What if chiropractic's expensive gamble ran amok in front of the estimated 450 million television viewers? What if it became a source of ridicule? "Hey, look at the poor eagle," Holmberg could hear the TV bozos guffawing, "The chiropractic eagle needs an adjustment. Ha! Ha! Ha!"

Holmberg listened to the assurances of Don Petersen and Mike Schroeder. There was nothing to worry about. There were backup systems da-da-da. In an interview with *Dynamic Chiropractic* about the float construction, the designer mentioned a tow bar "in case of emergency" and fire extinguishers as well as a fire drill.

*"What if the damn bird malfunctions and goes like this?"*

**The golden eagle's head drops to pass under the viaduct, then comes back into place**

wings had to be lowered to less than 18 feet in 60 seconds, then brought back up when the float had passed under the bridge.

"What if the damn bird malfunctions," Dr. Holmberg would ask, "and goes like this?" He'd screw up his body into a crude imitation of a deformed eagle with crumpled wings, head hanging to the side, eyes rolled back, tongue sticking out.

It wouldn't be the first time a float had broken down, to the humiliation of its builder and sponsor. Trucks were available all along the route to pull unfortunate entries out of the way to let the rest of the units go by.

After that Holmberg would lie awake nights, imagining the horror as the eagle exploded in flames, sending drivers, athletes and Lee Greenwood running for their lives. Chiropractors had thought the publicity from *"20/20"* was bad!

There was a small scare before the parade. As the hydraulic mechanism was being tested Sunday morning prior to the float judging, rotating the eagle ripped off some of the flowers. Petersen, Flaherty and a few others scrambled to reattach them before the critical-eyed parade officials drove up.

Things went fine early. The eagle rotated in all its white and golden splendor coming up Orange

Grove Boulevard, then turning right for the long run down Colorado Boulevard. No flowers fell off. Lee Greenwood, waving his arm to whip up enthusiasm, sang "God Bless the USA," and the athletes, Tiger Woods, Joe Morgan and Cathy Turner waved enthusiastically to the crowd.

The chiropractic contingent, most of them at the corner of Orange Grove and Colorado Boulevards, were justifiably proud. TV commentators extolled the float, its riders and chiropractic. Children pointed and cheered. Adults clapped and clicked their camera shutters. Somebody hollered, "Hey, there's Joe Morgan! Hey, Little Joe! Hey, Little Joe!"

had brought a football and started throwing it around, 10, 20, 30 yards. The street was packed with people. It was a game to see how far they could throw the football and catch it in the mob. The ball went out of control several times. Finally, it banged a woman in the head, and her husband confiscated it. Harsh words were exchanged. Things were getting ugly.

Finally the parade started again, and the folks ambled back to their lawn chairs on the sidelines.

Those waiting for the chiropractic float fixed their eyes on the viaduct. A float ahead of the eagle came along. Small talk stopped. Then somebody said,

Later on San Gabriel Boulevard, toward the end of the five-and-a-half mile parade route, only a few with special interest in chiropractic waited within sight of the ominous float-eating viaduct of Interstate 210, the so-called Foothill Freeway.

Suddenly, the parade stopped. The word raced down the line of spectators, "One of the floats broke down at the bridge!" Those waiting for the chiropractic float gasped. "Please don't let it be ours!" Visions of Holmberg's crippled eagle "goes like this" lurched to mind. "God help us!"

The crowd waited and got bored. People broke ranks and strolled into the street. Some young guys

"Here it comes." The eagle's head was down, ready to pass under the rusty steel understructure. So far so good. The eagle passed under the bridge without incident.

Would the eagle's head come back up? Steadily, the head and wings rose to their proper place, locked down, and the eagle resumed normal rotation. Somebody murmured, "All right."

People clapped when the chiropractic float approached, and they cheered when Lee Greenwood once more sang "God bless the U.S.A."

Everything had gone without a hitch. Piece of cake. That Holmberg. What a pessimist!

# A great afternoon for football

Many of the CCF board members and their families went to the Rose Bowl game after the Parade. It was a beautiful afternoon for football, with the sun shining on the mountains in the distance. The excitement and pageantry of the "granddaddy of bowl games" was thrilling, whatever the final score.

Perennial powerhouse Penn State was too much for Oregon, but most of the chiropractors couldn't care less about who won. They were there to enjoy each other's company and to cap off their Rose Parade experience. Except Dr. Lou Latimer, of course, who hails from Pennsylvania. When he wasn't cheering, he just sat there with a grin on his face.

"This whole thing – the party, the parade, the camaraderie – has been a great experience for me," he said. "To have Penn State win is frosting on the cake."

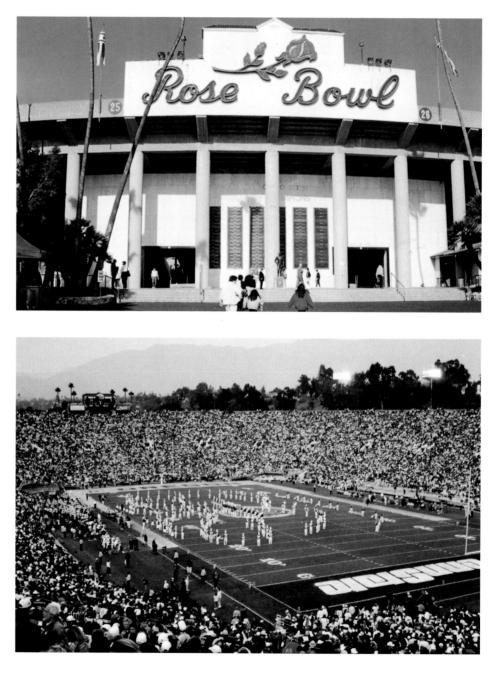

The venerable Rose Bowl — another aspect of the chiropractic New Year's activities that communicated a sense of history

54

# It doesn't rain on our parade, but it's close

The weather for the Rose Parade couldn't have been finer. Indeed, the weather the week before was sunny and cool, perfect for the arduous task of decorating the floats with millions of fragile flowers. It was clear and crisp on Monday, January 2, 1995, when the 110 units, including 54 floats, several bands and a variety of equestrian units began to roll, march and high-step along Orange Grove Boulevard.

It was jacket and sweater weather early, and some in the crowd felt a bit sorry for the majorettes and the float riders in skimpy outfits. The sky was the best of California blue with not a hint of the evil smog that people from elsewhere use to write off California as a nice place to visit but not to live. This was Pasadena paradise.

Good weather is a Rose Parade tradition. In the event's 105-year history, it has rained only nine times. The time people talk about was 1934, when 12 inches of rain fell in a short spell, sending Pasadena into chaos and even carving a new channel for the Los Angeles River. The Parade theme that year turned out to be most appropriate – "Tales of the Seven Seas."

But nine times in 105 years? Uncanny. The most common view holds that the decision not to have a Parade on the Sabbath has brought divine blessing. "He doesn't rain on our parade. We don't hold it on His day," explained Tournament of Roses president Mike Ward. Back in 1893 the Parade was first shifted to Monday to avoid a conflict with church services, and the tradition has continued since.

As the 1995 version of the Parade marched into history, the weather warmed a bit, and some of the jackets came off. The sun kept shining, and it was perfect football weather for the Penn State, Oregon clash at the Rose Bowl. Monday night, as the group of tired chiropractic celebrants retired to their hotels and began packing for early morning flights back east, the stars were shining.

The memories of the Rose Parade would be those of Glenda Wiese, a CCF trustee representing the Association for the History of Chiropractic: "To watch that golden eagle with its beautiful flowers coming up Colorado Boulevard with the bright blue sky overhead and the mountains in the background was something I'll never forget. It was simply a once-in-a-lifetime experience."

Early Tuesday morning, when the chiropractic contingent left for the airport, rain was leaking through the roof of the Pasadena Hilton parking garage. It was the start of several days of heavy rains that flooded streets and homes, causing mudslides and power outages and generally creating havoc in much of Southern California.

Timing is everything.

Skies remained clear immediately after the parade as thousands of people came to view the floats close up

# Rose Parade float – a big enough splash?

Even after the Rose Parade float project became an official part of CCF planning, Dr. William Holmberg told Mike Schroeder he thought the float was "a dumb idea." When he saw that the float could be a vehicle to help raise money, Holmberg modified his opinion.

Still, the float idea took some getting used to. A float in the Rose Parade seemed far removed from the everyday world of chiropractic. Some of the

*"The Chiropractic Foundation is celebrating a birthday, 100 years of good health."*

media chiro-bashing in the two years before the Centennial. Then there was the value of the Rose Parade television coverage.

"We were on the air for two minutes, with celebrities like Joe Garagiola talking about the benefits of chiropractic from a script we prepared," said Schroeder. "To buy two minutes on a single network would cost $1.8 million. So multiply that times five networks and we're talking

**NBC and the other television networks gave the parade and the chiropractic float good coverage**

planners and others wondered whether the money wouldn't be better spent on television advertising. "It's your flaky California type of thing," one chiropractor later observed.

Others understood that publicity is driven by events, not the routine in life. Certainly the profession could use positive publicity after the spate of

about $9 million worth of publicity." Not bad for a $250,000 investment.

An estimated 450 million television viewers heard the chiropractic message in 90 countries and 12 languages. Here's how John Beard, host for the FOX television network, conveyed it: "And it's the eagle with the majestic wingspread, (which) represents the

Chiropractic Centennial Foundation saluting America's and the world's athletes – many of whom, I'm sure, have made frequent trips to chiropractors. ... This year marks a century of chiropractic care."

Gayle Anderson, of Los Angeles television station KTLA, giving non-stop parade coverage in the nation's second largest television market, announced: "The Chiropractic Foundation is celebrating a birthday, 100 years of good health."

picture of the float in its city edition as part of its post-parade feature. "The newspapers really liked that eagle," Schroeder said.

Of course, nobody can say for sure what the float's real impact will be. Nobody knows how many chiropractors in the weeks after the parade heard their patients say, "Hey, I saw your float on television."

And who can measure the morale boost the chiropractic float gave chiropractors themselves? One

**Interviews with Lee Greenwood and Joe Morgan helped tell the chiropractic story**

Even before the parade began, the float was grabbing exposure. Prior to its coverage of the parade, KTLA featured the CCF entry in its parade preview show that included an interview with Joe Morgan and Lee Greenwood.

Newspapers also gave the float good coverage. For instance, the *Los Angeles Times* ran a large full-color

young doctor, a recent graduate of Life College, told a reporter: "I think this float is a great idea because it is a positive symbol. It shows that the profession can get itself together and take pride in what we collectively have accomplished. As far as I'm concerned, the float is worth every penny."

# The Scientific Symposium in Washington, D.C.

*It lived up to its billing as the greatest scientific conference ever staged by the chiropractic profession, but disappointing attendance took the edge off the enthusiasm and hammered the budget. Still, things said and done in Washington demonstrated positive aspects about chiropractic, including its level of research and a widespread confidence that the future could be bright.*

*"I think the future of chiropractic is assured."*

## "Chiropractic's greatest scientific symposium"

Chiropractors and their families who arrived early had opportunity to view a spectacular Fourth of July fireworks display in the nation's capital and take in a round of golf, but that and sightseeing were only preludes to the Centennial's first gala celebration.

The Washington, D.C., Centennial program was billed as "the greatest scientific symposium in the history of the profession." The opening plenary session and the concurrent tracks and workshops that followed demonstrated it would be just that.

Actor David Richards opened the program as D.D. Palmer, giving his history and introducing boys and girls carrying the flags of 60 countries where chiropractic is practiced 100 years after D.D.'s first chiropractic adjustment. Next Dr. William Holmberg, CCF president, applauded the coming together of the profession for the Centennial, called for recognition of the CCF trustees and advisory committee and asked for a moment of silence to recognize the chiropractic pioneers who had made the Grand Celebration possible.

David A. Chapman-Smith, Esq. was introduced as the one primarily responsible "for pulling together the entire educational portion of the Centennial." (Stefan Pallister, D.C., CCF program director, also deserved much of the credit.) Chapman-Smith then introduced Scott Haldeman, D.C., M.D., Ph.D., whose topic, "100 Years of Chiropractic Science," set the stage for the scientific presentations to follow.

Dr. Haldeman noted that more than 130 abstracts had been received and 95 original papers accepted for this symposium and that the speakers were "recognized as international leaders in the field of research." He underscored the importance of spinal research with the fact that it had helped produce guidelines on the care of the back and neck in the United States, the United Kingdom, Canada, Australia and New Zealand.

**Dr. Scott Haldeman set a positive tone for the research symposium**

CHIROPRACTIC

GRAND CELEBRATION 1995

In recounting the history of chiropractic research, Dr. Haldeman noted that there are six requirements for a scientific *milieu* to produce research – (1) commitment to science, which the profession had demonstrated since D.D. Palmer and B.J. Palmer; (2) establishment of well-equipped college clinical facilities, which was the case in both the United States and elsewhere in the world; (3) experimental and technical laboratories, which again the profession had in abundance; (4) establishment of research funding organizations, which chiropractic has in the FCER and other organizations; (5) competent and free-thinking mentors, among whom Haldeman mentioned B.J. Palmer, Fred Illie and Joe Janse, and (6) multiple, peer-reviewed scientific journals, of which the profession has several.

He reviewed some of the more exciting research projects and concluded by saying that chiropractic has a strong research *milieu*, that the level of research being performed is "very impressive," and because of that, "I think the future of chiropractic is assured."

The plenary session speakers that followed filled in many details about both the history and current state of research. The audience responded especially well to Professor Gordon Waddell, an M.D. from Glasgow, Scotland, who with humor and passion chronicled the failure of traditional medical treatment for low back pain. In describing "Modern Management of Spinal Disorders," Dr. Waddell called for a new clinical approach to back pain, where chiropractic would have a prominent role, and for a change in the entire health care system.

**Children with flags – symbolic of chiropractic's growth and potential worldwide**

Other speakers and their topics that first morning were Bjorn Rydevick, M.D., Ph.D., "Physiology of Spinal Nerve Compression," John Triano, D.C., M.A., "Advances in Biomechanical Research," and Rand Swensen, D.C., M.D., Ph.D., "Neurophysiological Basis for Chiropractic."

By the end of those first two hours the audience knew that the sessions to follow would be rich in solid information they could use in the field and that could boost their own confidence in the progress of chiropractic over its first 100 years.

David A. Chapman-Smith, Esq.

Dr. Bjorn Rydevick

Dr. Gordon Waddell

Dr. John Triano

Dr. Rand Swensen

# Get the big idea! Don't let it "get messed up"

Although the Washington sessions were heavily weighted toward science, chiropractic philosophy – as well as history, technique and a variety of professional issues like managed care – also received its rightful due.

The philosophy sessions were among the best-attended, with speakers offering both traditional and "contemporary" perspectives. The philosophy presentations on Thursday and a compelling debate on Friday turned into one of the solid successes of the Centennial experience. All that and continuing education credit hours too!

The room was packed for the session Thursday morning "Philosophy of Chiropractic – Historical Perspective" with Galen Price, D.C., and Virgil Strang, D.C., past and present presidents respectively of Palmer College of Chiropractic.

Dr. Price emphasized that philosophers of earlier days were like scientists of today, seeking for truth beyond mere opinions. "We marvel at D.D. Palmer's intellectual capacity to gather scientific data in his time (in various fields) to formulate an explanation, a philosophy, for the remarkable results we obtain when we adjust subluxated vertebrae." Price assured the crowd that chiropractic "has withstood the test of time" and reminded them of their responsibility to explain the importance of chiropractic to others, "to perpetuate our rich heritage."

Dr. Virgil Strang's energetic presentation exalted chiropractic philosophy as touching the essence of being, "the format for the way this universe ticks." Although cultural philosophy changes – Dr. Strang cited the abandoning of Hippocrates' *vis medicatrix naturae* and the increased role of the apothecary during the Industrial Revolution – chiropractic, he insisted, "is what it is anyhow." He echoed B.J. Palmer in describing chiropractic as "the big idea, from which all else – all else – follows! Never forget that, friends." He implored the audience not to allow philosophy to be de-emphasized in the profession.

Finally, Strang lifted the audience with the thought that as chiropractors they were not merely a tiny specialty in a sea of medical specialists but they, among all people, were in the best position to grasp the essence of being. The chiropractic philosophy they had been taught is the answer.

Later that day Guy Riekeman, D.C., was introduced as the man who might some day be recognized as "the father of wellness" because of his efforts in chiropractic patient education. His passionate presentation, enriched with quotations and readings, touched on three themes – the role of philosophy in bringing power to the profession, the need to live with integrity in congruency with that philosophy, and the importance of building loving relationships with other people, including family and friends.

Echoing Drs. Price and Strang, Dr. Riekeman told the standing-room-only crowd they should stop apologizing for their chiropractic philosophy. It has been vindicated, he assured them, by advances in scientific thought, such as those of Einstein and quantum physics, and even the medical community is beginning to recognize it.

In view of that, Riekeman urged the audience not to compromise themselves by restricting their role to back pain, thereby conforming to a health care system "on the brink of collapse." He agreed with medical doctors who predict managed care will be dead in five years "because the redirection of money is not improving health care for consumers,

and health care is a consumer-driven industry." He noted there were 37 million more patient visits to alternative care providers than to mainstream medicine, much of the payment for which came out of people's own pockets. "People will demand chiropractic care."

The real need, as Riekeman saw it, was the presentation of a new way of living and personal fulfillment. The chiropractic philosophy of wellness is not merely about preventing sickness but about empowering people to fulfill their potential.

That includes regaining passion in life, lost when incongruency exists between what people believe and how they live, a failure of personal integrity. He urged the chiropractors to stop worrying about personal failure and "start a conversation with society" about what chiropractic has to offer.

He recalled Walt Disney's farewell to his colleagues in which he urged them to "not let the dream get messed up." Similarly, chiropractors must not let the chiropractic dream get messed up. Finally, with all that chiropractors could offer humanity, they must remember family and friends. "Don't forget to love along the way."

A panel discussion on philosophy, moderated by Robert Mootz, D.C., included Gerard Clum, D.C., Robert Dubin, D.C., Andries Kleynhans, D.C., and James Winterstein, D.C. It was one of the Centennial's most thought-provoking sessions.

The first panelist, Dr. James Winterstein, president of National College of Chiropractic, urged his listeners to really analyze chiropractic philosophy rather than prop up old dogma with bits of new knowledge. Chiropractic philosophy, in Dr.

Winterstein's view, "should never be used as metaphysical explanation... nor as a method of boosterism." It should uplift and sustain the profession not demean it or other professions.

Dr. Gerard Clum, president of Life College of Chiropractic West, countered that philosophy provides a vital framework for everything chiropractors do, a rudder to determine their course in professional practice. Philosophy is reasserting itself as a cultural imperative, in some ways pushing aside the dominance of science, he said. He saw no reason to back away from "feeling a great sense of internal satisfaction that (the chiropractor) could bring for-

ward a perspective that could revolutionize the world."

Dr. Andries Kleynhans approached the subject from the standpoint of classical philosophy, noting that while chiropractic philosophy doesn't meet all the criteria for a body of philosophy in the classical sense, it contains many philosophical elements that need to be identified and fitted into a framework. Dr. Kleynhans proposed convening a group to decide on such philosophical questions, a suggestion met with enthusiasm by the other panelists.

Dr. Robert Dubin said his colleagues on the panel were making chiropractic philosophy too complicated. He encouraged the gallery to leave the philosophical debate and scientific pursuits to the academics, "to stick to the basics, helping sick people get well." He was educated that more is less. "Find it, fix it and leave it alone."

The moderator, Dr. Robert Mootz, stirred the pot with questions, which produced more sparring among the panelists. He invited their opinions on other topics, such as what could be done about the fragmentation within the profession.

Questions from the audience also stimulated discussion, such as one about the difference between the expressions "adjustment" and "manipulation." Dr. Clum argued there was a need to safeguard the lexicon of the profession. Dr. Winterstein responded there should be clearer definition of those terms, including clearly defined anatomical characteristics.

It was a spirited debate, but a friendly one, a good sign for a profession worried about division.

**Dr. Guy Riekeman urged the chiropractors to find personal fulfillment**

# McAndrews brothers relive Wilk battle

An enthusiastically received concurrent track on Thursday at the Washington symposium was the recounting by George McAndrews, Esq., and Jerome McAndrews, D.C., of their involvement in the Wilk trial.

Dr. Jerry McAndrews, with the American Chiropractic Association, drew a link between that historic trial and the need for research. In both cases the first battle was against apathy within the profession. "We need to get on with research," he asserted, because years after the Wilk victory, "there are still a million little boycotts out there trying to assert themselves against chiropractic in the marketplace."

plaintiffs accumulated more than a million documents, crossing the country to take 164 depositions, with some people under oath for as long as three weeks. Dr. McAndrews said George sometimes slept in his car in order to keep down the costs to the chiropractors.

The AMA, George McAndrews said, "was a formidable foe, and very ugly, very uncouth, very brutal, and in too many instances they succeeded in destroying the self-esteem" of good people in the chiropractic profession.

Yet the illegal boycott in restraint of trade was not only a crime against chiropractors but against medical

Dr. Jerry McAndrews and his lawyer-brother, George, share lessons from the Wilk trial

Urging the profession to break out of its "splendid isolation," Dr. McAndrews asked for all to "write a check for research" so that in the future they could hand a scientific study to anyone who questions the efficacy of what they do.

His brother, George McAndrews, a lawyer in Chicago, ended up representing the plaintiffs in the Wilk case after other Chicago law firms refused to accept it because of conflicts of interest. When asked if he would take the case, George had said, "I salivate at the prospect." His father and others in the family were chiropractors, and he had long been sensitive to the chiropractic cause. The job proved immense.

Eventually lawyers for Chester Wilk and the other

doctors as well, McAndrews said. Because the AMA excluded chiropractors as quacks, medical doctors couldn't teach chiropractic in their schools. Hundreds of thousands of physicians graduated from medical schools knowing nothing about the musculoskeletal system, to the detriment of their patients.

On a parallel track with his brother, George McAndrews called on chiropractors to meet the highest professional standards for the sake of future patients, "for the sake of our father's memory," and for the sake of future chiropractors like his youngest daughter, now a student at Cleveland Chiropractic College in Kansas City.

# New world of health care demands quality research

Friday morning's plenary session in Washington, "State of the Art," included research presentations on the clinical effectiveness of chiropractic. Dana Lawrence, D.C., from National College of Chiropractic, moderated the session.

Robert Brook, M.D., Sc.D., of the Rand Corporation, described changes in health care and how everyone must fit into them. In view of the shift to managed care, chiropractic needs better reporting of results, improved practice guidelines and more supportive research.

One study, by an all-chiropractic panel, found that one-third of the chiropractic manipulations for low back pain were inappropriate. Yet, he said, there reveals good success with chiropractic adjustments for headaches, but all the facts aren't in. Future projects should emphasize precision in categorizing the headache types investigated. Further, researchers should pay greater attention to design issues, thereby strengthening the validity of their studies. "If we receive praise, we should accept it with humility," he noted.

Alan Breen, D.C., Ph.D., dealt with "Clinical Effectiveness – Low Back Pain."

He noted that the effectiveness of treatment approaches has become an area of research methodology under increasingly critical review. "While there is a natural contest between reductionist sci-

Dr. Robert Brook

Dr. Nikolai Bogduk

Dr. Terry Yochum

is also need to have more scientific evidence for *underutilization* – how many people might have benefited from chiropractic adjustments but were not referred to chiropractors. Practice patterns, too, will need to change if chiropractors are to take on a primary care role.

Nikolai Bogduk, M.B., B.S.D., Ph.D., Dip. Anat., discussed rigorous procedures for precise diagnosis of chronic low back pain. He contradicted those with a "defeatist" attitude believing a diagnosis cannot be made in over 70 percent of such patients. Appropriate diagnostic technology is available if it will only be put to use.

Terry Yochum, D.C., D.A.C.B.R., related the history of diagnostic imaging and paid respects to pioneers in the field. "Digital imaging will eliminate film forever from radiology departments within five to 10 years."

Howard Vernon, D.C., F.C.C.S., discussed "Clinical Effectiveness for Headache" and gave an extensive view of the literature. The literature ence, which seeks the best technique, and the health care purchaser, who seeks the best patient-clinician match, the designers will need to be very clear about which master they are attempting to serve. ... Much progress has been made in our understanding of what is needed for a valid clinical trial of low back pain – progress which future research must incorporate to be viable."

James Weinstein, D.O., Ph.D., from the Department of Orthopaedic Surgery of the University of Iowa, described how the new paradigm of health care, in which politics, government and corporate America are playing more significant roles, will require increased collaborative research to provide measurement for clinical practices. Rather than leaving research to a few select researchers, he urged clinicians to submit data for others to share. Such data is demanded by the managed care system. The resulting abundance of data will be critical under managed care because "what can't be measured, can't be managed."

# Primary care physicians? Well, gynecologists aren't

One of the spunkiest sessions in Washington, and one that plucked emotional chords in the audience, was the debate on the proposition "Chiropractors Are Primary Care Physicians Not Primary Contact Specialists." This robust argument, which addressed head-on the question of how the profession will define itself, was orchestrated and moderated by David A. Chapman-Smith, LL.B.

Panelists supporting the proposition were Arnold Cianciulli, D.C., Meridel Gatterman, D.C., and John Hinwood, D.C. Panelists attacking the proposition were Craig Nelson, D.C., Susan Steward, D.C., and Gerald Weis, D.C. Chapman-Smith encouraged everyone to be "immoderate to get the issues out there." So they were.

Dr. Arnold Cianciulli launched the pro-motion side by attacking the definition of primary care physician offered by the Institutes of Medicine, an organization with no chiropractic representatives. "Why aren't we at the table? This is a loaded deck. We're playing into their hands by trying to redefine the way we practice."

has a concrete meaning and its prototype is the medical family practitioner, a generalist who provides a comprehensive list of diagnostic and therapeutic services. Gynecologists are also asking to be considered primary care physicians, he noted, but are losing the argument. "For chiropractors to be accepted as primary care physicians you'll have to prove yourselves more like family medical doctors than gynecologists are."

Dr. Meridel Gatterman, speaking for the proposition, observed that the majority of chiropractors see themselves as primary care physicians. "Luring chiropractors into believing we're primary contact specialists is semantic seduction."

Dr. Gatterman insisted that "our greatest strength is our patient-centered paradigm," rendering conservative natural therapy, working with patients as partners. The traditional chiropractic approach "is the essence of primary care."

Dr. Susan Steward from England voiced dismay that the issue was even being debated. She said in England and Europe chiropractors are muscu-

> *"If you win the rat race, you're still a rat."*

*Primary Care vs. Primary Contact panelists produced a no-holds-barred debate*

Dr. Cianciulli painted a gloomy picture of fewer chiropractors and closed chiropractic colleges resulting from trying to fit into managed care in a limited role. "I urge you to believe in yourselves, to walk tall. Don't be mesmerized."

Dr. Craig Nelson came out firing. He described Cianciulli's argument as unwinnable because "the idea that chiropractors are primary care physicians is not taken seriously" by the public and policy makers. He said the expression "primary care physician"

loskeletal specialists and respected as such. Sometimes when she visits America she is embarrassed to admit she is a chiropractor because chiropractors are known for "fleecing their patients." She said a lawyer friend told her to expect more lawsuits against U.S. chiropractors for doing things they're not trained to do. "You're in danger of becoming a jack of all trades and master of none."

Dr. John Hinwood, from Australia, said chiropractors there also have respect but as primary care physicians. Although that country has socialized medicine, chiropractors don't rely on it. "In practice there are reasons or results. Patients pay for results. Patients pay cash for results. If you don't perform, you're not in business." He urged chiropractors to avoid a system that treats diseases and not patients. "If you win the rat race, you're still a rat."

The final presenter against the motion was Dr. Gerald Weis, who has responsibilities in several managed care and multidisciplinary organizations in Cincinnati. He reported high rates of referrals from medical doctors, who "are excited about dealing with chiropractors who understand their role as specialists." He described his nightmare where a bus pulls out leaving chiropractors arguing on the corner. He noted that chiropractors perform 94 percent of spinal manipulations and that 87 percent of chiropractic visits are for musculoskeletal problems. "If that's true, what are we waiting for?"

Chapman-Smith invited more vigorous exchanges, including opinions from the audience. When time ran out, he called for an audience vote on which side they favored. The vote was overwhelming for the proposition that chiropractors should remain primary care physicians. Chapman-Smith, perhaps tongue in cheek, declared the debate a draw.

The issue - how the profession will define itself

# Seek interdependence, Covey tells chiropractors

One of highlights of the Washington Centennial program was the appearance of Stephen Covey, a popular lecturer on personal and corporate growth, and author of the best-selling book, *The 7 Habits of Highly Effective People*. CCF planners saw an appropriate chiropractic application of his main theme – interdependence is a higher value than independence.

In the sessions Friday, Covey reviewed his seven principles and made applications to chiropractic. He encouraged the chiropractors to develop personal mission statements, which he distinguished from goals. "Too many have climbed to the top of the ladder of success only to find that the ladder was leaning against the wrong wall."

He provided tips on time management as well, encouraging his audience to devote time to things that may not seem urgent but are ultimately more important to one's personal fulfillment. One of his slides indicated that the most successful executives spend 65 to 80 percent of their time on those important areas.

At the core of the Covey message, though, was the importance of rising through personal accomplishment to the state of interdependence. For private victory, Covey listed, "Be Proactive, Begin with the End in Mind, and Put First Things First." Covey's three habits vital to interdependence are:

**There is something greater to be had than independence, Stephen Covey told the chiropractors**

- "Thinking win/win." The course of action must benefit both parties. Interestingly, Covey insisted, "only one person has to think win–win for there to be success."

- "Seeking first to understand, then to be understood." Empathetic listening, which he defined as listening within the other person's frame of reference, would be useful in relating to patients. "The more you listen the more you can influence."

- "Synergize." Covey decried the undeveloped potential in many people's lives because of their inability to relate to others. There is an implicit message for the profession: As the health care marketplace becomes more and more heavily structured, with insurance, gatekeepers, case managers and other factors separating the patient from the provider, the challenge for chiropractors is to gain access to and work within a system that is foreign to their experience and orientation.

The last of the seven habits, "Sharpening the Saw," refers to constant examination of oneself and refinement of one's behavior.

Covey supplied attendees with a booklet that illustrated the seven habits plus concepts like the difference between values and principles, leadership, building trust, developing "the fire within," extending one's circle of influence and the conditions of empowerment.

The audience's response to Covey was positive. In conversations after the sessions, several participants expressed their opinion that Covey's kind of thinking is precisely what the profession needs.

# Parker, Williams urge love, "inner eye"

The session "Reflections of My Life in Chiropractic" in the Washington program brought together on the same platform for the first time in 38 years two living giants of chiropractic, Drs. James Parker and Sid Williams. They regaled the packed room with personal anecdotes and plenty of encouragement to keep up the spizzerinctum.

Dr. Parker pleaded with the crowd to get back to basics and include love, "the quality," along with the nerve "quantity flow" written about by B.J. Palmer. "You were born to help one patient at a time." As long as generations of chiropractors will do that, he said, "you will always win because you will always serve."

In a similar vein, Dr. Williams urged the crowd to "get centered in your practice." He told them not to worry about managed care "because the public will not put up with it." Work for "any willing provider" laws as the solution, he urged, and above all, "get the vision, the creative eye, the inner eye. ...You've got to believe to be successful."

Dr. Sid Williams

Dr. James Parker

# "You'll have to live with managed care"

Saturday morning's plenary session in Washington, moderated by Dr. Carl S. Cleveland, III, provided answers to one of the biggest questions for chiropractors, the impact of managed care. Not everything reported was bleak for chiropractic by any means, but one thing came through loud and clear: Health care delivery is changing dramatically and to succeed in the new environment chiropractors will have to adapt.

In "The Future of Health Care," Russell Coile, Jr., D.C., portrayed health care reform no longer as an initiative by the federal government but as happening nonetheless through managed care. However, managed care is neither uniform in its structure nor particularly stable. He described how

Dr. Russell Coile, Jr.

HMOs may go through various stages with the direction being toward greater price competition and more provider control. He predicted that by the year 2,000 chiropractic will be included in most of the managed care programs.

Marion McGregor, D.C., Msc., discussed "Education and Research," assuring the audience that "managed care is here to stay. The days of simply taking care of patients and getting paid for it are gone." In the new world, doctors' services will be reviewed by peers or others, and to continue to provide services the chiropractor will have to demonstrate successful outcomes. Properly designed, interdisciplinary research studies that can produce consumable data will be vital in establishing the profession in the new health system. She

*"The days of simply taking care of patients and getting paid for it are gone."*

noted that the individual practitioner will have to "learn to live with uncertainty," which will require, among other things, "being a life-long learner."

Robert Mootz, D.C., F.I.C.C., addressed "Impact of Health Policy in Chiropractic." He echoed the other speakers about managed care's impact, noting that the credibility and judgment of doctors would be constantly challenged. The emphasis will be on guidelines, outcomes and accountability. Chiropractors must have critical appraisal skills to determine accuracy in labeling and process all the information that will come their way. He warned that no one will be able "to sit on the sidelines and throw rocks" at the system. He ended on an upbeat note, "incredibly optimistic" because he believes

Dr. Marion McGregor

chiropractic is ahead of many other specialty groups now jockeying for position.

The topic of Arthur White, M.D., was "Integration of Chiropractic in Managed Care in a Multidisciplinary Setting." He praised the chiropractors for their wholistic approach and assured them there were places available in the new environment. "M.D.s know they need to join multidisciplinary networks that include chiropractors." He noted there would be a place both for the "super specialist" and for others who would expand their services as generalists. "You're great gatekeepers," he told the audience. However, to succeed, chiropractors, like other doctors, will have to work within the system and demonstrate accountability. In the final analysis, he pointed out, the doctors who will survive in the marketplace will focus on "what's best for the patient and not for the pocketbook."

William Meeker, D.C., M.P.H., discussed "Future Impact of Guidelines," describing their direct and indirect effects. Guidelines will be required, but the establishment of such guidelines will compel doctors of chiropractic to work with organized groups, something at odds with the individualistic history of the profession. Dr. Meeker suggested the development of practice guidelines will promote dialogue and help unify the profession and much of health care practice.

In "Meeting the Challenges of Private Practice," David Kats, D.C., provided details of the impact of the managed care environment on income, noting that the cash practice, perhaps limited to more secluded areas, would in most cases be at a distinct disadvantage. "In the past patients had their choice of cash practitioners. In the future the choice will be between one doctor where he will have to pay cash and another with a managed care organization where he can get comparable care for free." He said he envisioned plenty of interdisciplinary clinics and referrals, mentioning one large chiropractic clinic that has been employing M.D.s.

Dr. William Meeker

Dr. Robert Mootz

# History sessions feature chiropractic scholars

History was featured in Davenport but also well represented in Washington, D.C. Historian Russ Gibbons moderated a panel there on "50 Years of Chiropractic, 1945-1995," featuring panelists Gibbons described as the foremost scholars about the profession. On the panel were Walter Wardwell, Ph.D., Joseph Keating, Jr., Ph.D., and William S. Rehm, D.C.

The same day (Thursday) there was a history workshop in which Dr. Keating joined Glenda Wiese, CCF trustee for the AHC, to discuss "How to Capture History."

Another specialized topic was "A History of Chiropractic in Sports," moderated by Tom Hyde, D.C., and featuring panelists Jan Corwin, D.C., John Danchick, D.C., Leroy Perry, D.C., and Philip Santiago, D.C.

Still another was "History of Black Chiropractors," moderated by Hubert Whelchel, D.C., with panelists, Herman J. Glass, II, D.C., and Cal B. Whitworth, D.C. Dr. Bobby Westbrooks was scheduled as moderator but passed away before the Washington program.

# Concurrent tracks offer something for everyone

The concurrent tracks each day of the Washington symposium offered something for just about everybody in chiropractic. Original research papers were presented in seven separate tracks, making the Washington symposium a once-in-a-lifetime experience for those interested in how science can advance the profession. Here are some of the other topics and presenters, as listed in the CCF program, in order of presentation:

**Thursday**
Business Management – David Kats, D.C., Karl Parker, D.C.; Vertebral Subluxation Complex and Theories of Chiropractic – Robert Leach, D.C., Andries Kleynhans, D.C., Charles Lantz, D.C., Dale Nansel, D.C., Reed Phillips, D.C.; Chiropractic Assistants Program – Pat Atanas; Associated Persons Program – Michele Hoffman; ACRRT Program – Dennis Marchiori, D.C.; Clinical Grand Rounds: Lumbar Spine – Sil Mior, D.C., Joel Carmichael, D.C., James Cox, D.C., Adrian Grice, D.C., Larry Wyatt, D.C.; Technique Grand Rounds Part 1 – Tom Bergmann, D.C., Kevin Bartol, D.C., Nelson De Camp, D.C., Gary Jacob, D.C., Gregory Plaugher, D.C.; Business Management – Noel Lloyd, D.C., Charles Ward, D.C.; Chiropractic Assistants Program – Sherry Hodge; Associated Persons Program – Jeanine Graykowski, Martha Dehn; Business Management – Richard Vincent, D.C., Larry Markson, D.C.; Documenting Effectiveness of Chiropractic Care – Malik Slosberg, D.C., Craig Nelson, D.C.; Chiropractic Assistants/ACRRT Program – Robert Percuoco, D.C.; Associated Persons Program – Sandra Phillips.

**Friday**
ACCRT Program – Garry Krakos, D.C.; Issues in Chiropractic Education and Licensure – Meredith Bakke, D.C., Carl S. Cleveland, III, D.C., Reed Phillips, D.C., Paul Tullio, D.C., Robert Vaughan, D.C.; Clinical Grand Rounds: Cervical Spine – Rand Swensen, D.C., Peter Aker, D.C., Arthur Croft, D.C., Stephen Foreman, D.C., Ronald Gitelman, D.C., Craig Nelson, D.C., Gary Tarola, D.C.; Technique Grand Rounds Part 2 – Tom Bergmann, D.C., Kevin Bartol, D.C., James Cox, D.C., Arlan Fuhr, D.C., Warren Hammer, D.C., Adrian Grice, D.C.; Chiropractic Terminology – Meridel Gatterman, D.C., Charles Masarsky, D.C.; Business Management: Grand Rounds – Richard Vincent, D.C., David Kats, D.C., Noel Lloyd, D.C., Larry Markson, D.C., Karl Parker, D.C., Charles Ward, D.C.; Ligamentous Failure in the Cervical Spine: The Domino Theory – Stephen Foreman, D.C., Michael Stahl, D.C.; Chiropractic Rehabilitation in a Multidisciplinary Setting – Kim Christensen, D.C., Don Fitz-Ritson, D.C., John Triano, D.C.; Chiropractic Assistants Program – Paul Peterson, D.C.; Associated Persons Program – Kaye Rive.

**Saturday**
Imaging for Chiropractors in Their Second Century – Reed Phillips, D.C., Gary Guebert, D.C., Andrew Jackson, D.C., Norman Kettner, D.C., John Taylor, D.C., Terry Yochum, D.C.; Managed Care Speakers – Dan Hansen, D.C., Rick Flaherty, Jay Gillis, D.C., Lawrence Jack, D.C., Douglas Metz, D.C.; Whiplash: Principles and Introduction to Management – Arthur Croft, D.C.; Chiropractic Assistants Program – Carla Vincent; Associated Persons Program – Sandra Kindred.

# Dozens of workshops enhance chiropractic knowledge

Workshops throughout the Washington symposium included the following, as listed in the official CCF program, by order of presentation:

**Technique**: Activator Method – Arlan Fuhr, D.C.; Blair – R. Weldon Muncy, D.C.; Gonstead – Doug Cox, D.C.; Motion Palpation – Keith Innes, D.C.; Cox – James Cox, D.C.; SOT – Vern Hagen, D.C.; Thompson – Miriam Shultz, D.C.; McKenzie Method – Gary Jacob, D.C.; Applied Kinesiology – George Goodheart, D.C.; BEST – Ted Morter, D.C.; NUCCA – Albert Berti, D.C.; Atlas Orthogonality – Roy Sweat, D.C.; Kale Procedures in Clinical Practice – Michael Kale, D.C.; CBP – Donald Harrison, D.C.; Myofascial – Warren Hammer, D.C.; Motion Assisted Adjusting (Leander) – Dennis Semlow, D.C.; Toggle Recoil – John Strazewski, D.C.

**Examination & Management**: Orthotics – Kent Greenawalt and Monte Greenawalt, D.C.; Osteoporosis – Francisco Diez Gurtugay, D.C.; Temporomandibular Joint – Darryl Curl, D.C.; Differential Diagnosis of LBP – Rand Swensen, D.C.; Extremities – David Pierson, D.C.; Imaging 1/Plain Film – John Taylor, D.C.; Orthopedic & Neurologic Exam – Kevin McCarthy, D.C.; Women's Health Issues – James Browning, D.C., Patricia Brennan, Ph.D., Maria Hondras, D.C.; Laboratory Diagnosis – Alan Adams, D.C.; Therapeutic Muscle Stretching – Brian Nook, D.C.; Care During Pregnancy – Joan Fallon, D.C.;

General Physical Exam – Gary Tarola, D.C.; Imaging 2/CT/MRI/Videofluoroscopy – Terry Yochum, D.C., Alan Breen, D.C.

**Basic Sciences**: Spinal Anatomy – Gregory Cramer, D.C.; Cervicogenic Pain – Nikolai Bogduk, M.D., Howard Vernon, D.C.; Imaging Normal Spinal Anatomy – Norman Kettner, D.C.; Spinal Neurophysiology and Somatovisceral Reflexes – Scott Haldeman, D.C., Bernadette Murphy, D.C.; Barbara Polus, B.App.Sc.(Chiro).

**Special Topics**: Disability Evaluation – Larry Swank, D.C; How to Capture History – Glenda Wiese, M.A., Joseph Keating, Jr., Ph.D.; Record Keeping – Louis Sportelli, D.C., Michael Pedigo, D.C.; Scientific Literature 1/Critical Appraisal – Marion McGregor, D.C.; Biomechanics of the Adjustment – John Triano, D.C.; Case Reports – Sil Mior, D.C.; Cervical Spine Trials – Peter Aker, D.C.; Contraindications and Complications – Gregory Plaugher, D.C., Allan Terrett, B.App.Sc.(Chiro); Ergonomics – Scott Donkin, D.C.; Lumbar Biomechanics – Alan Breen, D.C.; Health Care Reform – Charles Sawyer, D.C.; Monitoring Results – William Meeker, D.C., Dan Hansen, D.C.; Rehabilitation – Kim Christensen, D.C.; Scientific Literature 2/Finding What You Want – Deb Callahan, D.C., Ronald Rupert, D.C.; Psychosocial Factors in Practice – Curtis Rexroth, D.C.; Report Writing & Correspondence – David A. Chapman-Smith, LL.B.

# Colleges hold parties as part of Washington gala

While the CCF organized the entertainment for Thursday and Saturday nights of the Washington gala, several chiropractic colleges held well-attended social receptions on Friday evening, some featuring live bands and entertainment. Receptions included those by the Cleveland Chiropractic Colleges, Life Chiropractic College, Los Angeles College of Chiropractic, National College of Chiropractic, and a joint reception by Palmer College of Chiropractic and Palmer College of Chiropractic West.

**Talk about standing out in a crowd...**

# Museum exhibit shows how chiropractic grew

Sofya Belair

*"What makes this exhibit unique... is that it covers the entire history of the profession."*

**Viewing the historical exhibit enhances understanding of how chiropractic has developed**

One of the CCF's goals, met with flying colors, was to create a museum-quality exhibit on the history of chiropractic. The finished product, representing a collaboration with the Association for the History of Chiropractic, was a big hit in the exhibit halls at Washington, D.C., and Davenport.

Significant developments during chiropractic's 100-year history were carefully researched and professionally mounted in text and photographs on five specially built birch and walnut panels. Historical artifacts came from private collections and college archives.

"What makes this exhibit unique and historically significant is that it covers the entire history of the profession, including people, events, schools, tables and equipment, legislation and professional organizations," said curator R. Sofya Belair. "Nothing of this magnitude has ever been done before."

The exhibit includes five two-sided wooden panels, with 18 smaller panels for which each CCF-member college designed its own historical exhibit.

Each side of the five panels is devoted to a decade in chiropractic history, and two other panels cover antecedents to chiropractic and a profile of D.D. Palmer.

In 1994 Ms. Belair was brought on as curator for the project, which was initially proposed by trustee Glenda Wiese. Ms. Belair spent three months researching and writing the text, and another six months traveling to colleges to collect photographs and artifacts. Table manufacturers loaned several of the 13 tables displayed.

A virtue of the exhibit was its succinct and objective presentation of chiropractic's historical development. "When you take the time to read all this," one observer in Davenport's RiverCenter commented, "you understand why chiropractic is what it is."

Here is a segment entitled, "American Medicine in the Nineteenth Century":

*Chiropractic may be seen as an answer to the deficiencies in medical concepts that existed throughout most of the*

74

nineteenth century. Physicians would commonly treat their patients with harsh curatives which often did nothing to help, or produced harmful side effects. As a result, a populist rebellion against the medical profession grew and brought forth a desire for safer forms of treatment.

Popular alternative health care movements included Thomsonism, Grahamism, Homeopathy, Eclectic Medicine, Christian Science, Osteopathy, Physical Culture and Chiropractic.

The exhibit makes it clear that the chiropractic profession is more than a product of its philosophy. It is also a product of economic and social developments, and how the profession reacted was critical. The section on the decade of 1925-1935 included these observations:

*The Depression took a terrible toll on chiropractors and chiropractic students, and the student population of* chiropractic schools took a dramatic plunge. Within the profession there was both organizational and educational dissent at every level.

*The first non-profit and professionally owned institutions came into being during this time, and educational standardization commenced when the National Chiropractic Association created the Committee on Education Standards.*

*Historian Russell W. Gibbons writes, "Chiropractic took a surprise turn during this time towards true reform of its training institutions and began to make changes within its professional organizational structure that would eventually bring it respect as a true profession rather than a marginal profession."*

After the Centennial, some of the loaned items were returned, but the remainder of the exhibit is stored at Palmer College. It is available for use by others upon arrangement.

**Chiropractic is more than a product of its philosophy**

# So Excited

The Pointer Sisters,
a small band and
an explosion of
joyous energy

Photograph by
Wanda Simmons

# Pointer Sisters, other talent get gala crowd "So Excited"

The entertainment for the Washington gala was a good blend. Along with showcase entertainment Thursday and Saturday on the big stage, several performers entertained in the exhibit hall. The entertainment offered humor, a chiropractic slant and the high energy of the Pointer Sisters.

Thursday night featured the Capitol Band, a military concert band in red and black uniforms, playing songs like "Stars and Stripes Forever" appropriate to Washington, D.C.

Comedian Ron Klonel, a retired chiropractor, acted as emcee, did some of his own routines, and played a videotape of David Letterman's infamous "Signs You've Gone to a Bad Chiropractor." They included "No. 10 – When you walk you make a wacky accordion sound, No. 9 – Keeps saying a spine is like a box of chocolates, No. 3 – Rushes in still wearing his Burger King uniform, and No. 1 – You're fully clothed and he's naked."

Dr. Elaine Dembe did a chiropractic rap song. Dr. Klonel got Cindy (Mrs. Michael) Hulsebus into one bit and four CCF representatives into another. The latter skit featured Rick Flaherty, Dr. Roger Hulsebus, David A. Chapman-Smith, Esq. and Dr. Lou Latimer, each with wigs or goofy caps. "What can be said about this group," Klonel asked, "that hasn't been said about hemorrhoids?"

The main attraction Thursday night was The Capitol Steps, a troupe of former Congressional staffers whose "aim is to be funnier than the

*"Remember – the truth, like chiropractic, is incontrovertible."*

**Chiropractic comedian Ron Klonel and some good sports**

From left, David A. Chapman-Smith, Rick Flaherty, Dr. Roger Hulsebus, Dr. Lou Latimer

Congress." Their comical and musical routines mocked Bill and Hillary Clinton, Newt Gingrich, Bob Dole, Teddy Kennedy, Bob Packwood and other figures like O.J. Simpson, Bob Dylan, Mick Jagger and Keith Richards of the Rolling Stones, Lorena Bobbett, and Phil Donahue. One of the numbers brought in CCF trustees Drs. Kerwin Winkler and Michael Hulsebus as computer geeks.

Saturday was the big entertainment night, with amateur chiropractic talent followed by Alan Thicke and the Pointer Sisters. Emcee David Richards as D.D. Palmer introduced the Chiro Cools, seven chiropractors and three chiropractic wives, whose songs, both humorous and serious, saluted chiropractic. A highlight was the appearance of Andrea Pack, 10-year-old daughter of two of the Cools, Ken Pack, D.C., and Heidi Pack. Andrea signed for the deaf to Lee Greenwood's "God Bless the USA." The other Chiro Cools are Fred P. Dehn, D.C., Marti A. Dehn, Ron Geiger, D.C., Lynn Geiger, D.C., John R. Kosbau, D.C., T. Laura Kosbau, D.C., Pat McWilliams, D.C., and Cindy Wells. The Chiro Cools left the audience with the message: "Remember – the truth, like chiropractic, is incontrovertible. Malice may attack it. Ignorance may deride it. But in the end, there it is."

Alan Thicke was in fine form in Washington

Drs. Kerwin Winkler and Michael Hulsebus as computer geeks

Denise Diangelo Jones, a professional song writer and performer and a student at Life College, saluted chiropractic with original compositions. She painted a musical picture of a time when the world will recognize what chiropractic has, when people everywhere will be able "to turn on the power, turn on the light."

A chiropractic quartet from Canada, Acappella, was up next, performing a variety of close-harmony romantic and popular songs. Acappella members are Dr. Gary Adams, Dr. Bob Pike, Richard Whitmore and Murray Adams.

Then D.D. brought on comedian Alan Thicke, who had already endeared himself to the profession for his performance at the Davenport kickoff. Thicke sang snippets of several songs he has written for tele-

vision shows and delivered a string of well received jokes and one-liners.

The Fabulous Pointer Sisters finished off the evening with their repertoire of high energy tunes including "I'm So Excited" (a kind of theme song for the Centennial played at the kickoff), "Hot Together," "Automatic," "Slow Hand," "He's So Shy" and "Neutron Dance." When they finished up with "Jump!" the crowd was standing and clapping in the aisles and in front of the stage.

Others who entertained in Washington included Dr. Daniel Davidson, Dr. Scott Durbin, Dr. David Koffman, David D'Angelo, Philip & Alicia Yochum, Trish Kelly-Knight and Dr. Robert Zachary Rush.

Tickling the funny bone

Acappella

A memory for Dr. and Mrs. Michael Hulsebus and Kristina Bemis

Ron Klonel and Mrs. Michael (Cindy) Hulsebus

The Chiro Cools and special member Andrea Pack (inset)

# Despite low attendance, Washington gala will shape the future

Getting 2,000 people together for a chiropractic scientific symposium was a landmark accomplishment in the history of the profession. The problem was the CCF hoped and planned for more, and when the greater number didn't show, it took a toll on the budget, the comfort level of exhibitors and the planners' morale. It also forced a cutback on the quality of the Davenport gala.

Holding a convention in the nation's capital proved to be at least double the cost of the one in chiropractic's birthplace. The Washington Convention Center was pricey, the cost of setup and audio visual equipment likewise. The program was also very ambitious, with high-priced presenters like Stephen Covey and top-level entertainment like the Pointer Sisters. Surveys indicating people would support the event proved bogus, and the CCF budget plummeted into the red.

*"Chiropractic's leading researchers felt they had been given special recognition."*

The Washington, D.C. Convention Center

It was a major blow to the confidence of the CCF board. There was bitterness on the part of some, who described it as "a shame," a "bittersweet experience" and "our biggest mistake." One trustee admitted: "Washington should never have happened. It was not the right theme for celebrating a birthday nor the time. It was only a political move within the CCF."

A CCF committee chairman: "For those who attended this program, the rating was very high, from start to finish. The low attendance was disappointing in that the week before in the same location 8,000 physical therapists were in attendance. I had hoped that this profession would rise up, in force, and send a message to Washington that chiropractic is strong. This was my disappointment."

David A. Chapman-Smith, Esq. , who had invested so much of his time, energy and hope into putting on the "most sophisticated academic and entertainment program ever mounted by the profession," was deeply disappointed. Yet, as he reflected on the Washington symposium, he concluded it would still prove to be important for the profession.

"Chiropractic's leading researchers, often left out of the limelight in the past, occupied pride of place and felt they had been given special recognition in the Centennial year. For them this was the best attended and most stimulating research meeting ever. These researchers have a major leadership role to play during the next 10 to 20 years, and the experience of Washington, D.C., gave them new enthusiasm.

"Equally important for the future of the profession, lecturers and guests in Washington included medical leaders from North America, Europe, Australia, China, Hong Kong and the Russian Federation. These included important figures such as Dr. James Weinstein, editor of *Spine*, the leading back pain researcher from the UK, Dr. Gordon Waddell, and Dr. Mikheev, director, Occupational Health Office, World Health Organization.

Planning and worrying

"These influential decision-makers left Washington, D.C., with an extremely positive image of the role and importance of the chiropractic profession, and there is no question that this will produce major dividends in the years ahead."

Dr. Carl S. Cleveland, III, had similar feelings: "Except for the financial issue, the low attendance only hurt those who did not attend. It was the pro-

fession's scientific conference of our lifetimes. Never have more scientists, clinicians and academicians come together on the podium to present, discuss and debate the science, philosophy and art of chiropractic."

Here's how Dr. Robert A. Brooks, a prominent chiropractor from Tulsa, Oklahoma, put things into perspective: "My daddy used to say that, if you were going to throw a party, make sure it is the kind that people who didn't attend would wish they had. That's what happened here. It was a wonderful party in every way."

**Numbers registering in Washington were disappointing**

**Plenty of exhibitors, too little traffic**

# Chiropractic researchers win CCF contest grants

The Chiropractic Centennial Foundation had as one of its original goals the sponsoring of chiropractic research, and a contest with cash prizes was the way to do it. Two grants were awarded in clinical science, one in basic science and two in private practice clinical science, for a total of $40,000. The awards were announced before the Centennial year and presented during the gala celebration.

Open Basic Science Award ($10,000) – "Neck EMG Changes Associated with Meningeal Inflammation": James Hu, Ph.D., assistant professor of dentistry, University of Toronto; Howard Vernon, D.C., professor, Canadian Memorial Chiropractic College; Chih-Mong Tsai, D.D.S., graduate student, faculty of Dentistry, University of Toronto.

Clinical Science Awards ($10,000 each) – "Randomized Clinical Trial of Chiropractic Adjustments and Massage Treatment for Essential Hypertension": Gregory Plaugher, D.C., assistant professor, Palmer College of Chiropractic West; William Meeker, D.C., M.P.H., dean of research, Palmer West; Kenneth Courtney, Ph.D., professor, Palmer West; Edward Cremata, D.C., private practice, Fremont, California; Mark Lopes, D.C., private practice, Fremont, California. "Criterion-Related Validity of Manual Diagnostic Maneuvers for Spine Pain Patients": John Triano, M.A., D.C., Texas Back Institute; Mark Doyne, M.D., Texas Back Institute; Marion McGregor, D.C., M.Sc., F.C.C.S, private chiropractic research consultant.

Private Practice Clinical Science Awards ($5,000 each) – "Comparison of Chiropractic and Medical Therapy Utilizing ROM Exercises in Chronic Neck Pain Patients": Larry Morries, D.C., D.A.C.A.N., Englewood, Colorado; John Sbarbaro, M.D., director, Colorado Prevention Center; Allen Prochazka, M.D., Englewood, Colorado. "The Efficacy of Cervical Manipulation (Toggle Recoil Technique) for Chronic

Several awards were given for research. Here Dr. Carl S. Cleveland, III, left, and Dr. Scott Haldeman present an award to James Hu, Ph.D.

Headaches with Upper Cervical Joint Dysfunction": W. Whittingham, B.App.Sc.(Chiro), Melbourne, Australia; R. English, B.A., Dip.Ed., B.App.Sc. (Chiro), Melbourne, Australia; G. Littlejohn, M.D., M.B.B.S. (Hons.), F.R.C.P., F.R.C.R.P., M.P.H., Melbourne Australia.

"There were 51 proposals received for the awards," said Carl S. Cleveland, III, D.C., chairman of the CCF education committee. "Our judges, Tony Rosner, Ph.D., FCER director of research, and Scott Haldeman, D.C., M.D., Ph.D., chair of the World Federation of Chiropractic (WFC) research council, had tough decisions to make. We wished there could have been more awards." Judges focused particularly on experimental design, quality of writing and relevance to the proposal to chiropractic, he said.

## Interdenominational prayers

Dr. Glenn M. Hultgren served as the CCF official chaplain. Interdenominational prayers were held each morning during both the Washington and Davenport symposiums.

## Continuing education credits

The CCF conference in Washington was approved for continuing education credits in all states except Ohio and Oklahoma. The total credit available over the entire program was 16.5 hours.

**The Pointer Sisters got the chiropractic audience to "Jump!"**

# Telling the Story of Chiropractic Care

*The Centennial provided a hook to catch media attention about the virtues of chiropractic, and the profession mobilized itself to get the word out with a goal of one billion media impressions. The dream of telling the chiropractic story on television through a documentary held special appeal, but getting the job done was a daunting task.*

*"Chiropractic is much closer to understanding that the body is the function of its intelligence."*

## TV documentary – crown jewel of the Centennial

For many in both the CCF leadership and the profession's rank and file, the chiropractic documentary was the crown jewel of all the sparkling Centennial projects. "From Simple Beginnings" explores the growth and antagonism between wellness philosophy and the medical approach to treating the sick. The documentary's premise is that treating only sickness has proved inadequate and costly. The time has come for the philosophy of wellness, and the chiropractic profession is prepared to lead the way.

Popular and highly credible TV host Jack Perkins does the on-camera and voice-over narration, and a variety of health care leaders, including prestigious non-chiropractors, give comments on camera. Probably the one likely to grab the most viewer attention is Deepak Chopra, M.D., the best-selling author and lecturer whose beyond-mechanism philosophy parallels certain aspects of chiropractic. His comments, quoted many times throughout the program, include references to "the body's inner intelligence" and "the superstition of materialism." At one point Dr. Chopra states that chiropractors have a better understanding of the origins and force of life than do other health care practitioners. "Chiropractic is much closer to understanding that the body is the function of its intelligence."

**Getting ready for the video shoot**

**Interviews for the documentary required many hours and a lot of travel**

Dean Black, Ph.D., an author and lecturer about health care philosophy, also makes powerful points in explaining how vitalism was crowded out by the atomistic philosophy of Isaac Newton, warning that antibiotics could prove to be a major scourge, and underscoring the high failure rate of medical procedures. He asks, "If we have a health care system, why do we have to lose our health in order to enter that system?"

Chiropractic college presidents add their insights about chiropractic and the extensive education chiropractors receive. Included are Carl S. Cleveland, III, D.C., Gerard Clum, D.C., Thomas Gelardi, D.C., George Goodman, D.C., Virgil Strang, D.C., Sid Williams, D.C., and James Winterstein, D.C. "Man-on-the-street" interviews offer opinions about the inadequacy of the present health system and the effectiveness of chiropractic care.

The documentary script, written by Dr. Guy Riekeman and Jim Hancock, traces the develop- ment of wellness philosophy since ancient times (especially as articulated by Hippocrates), devotes several minutes to the history of chiropractic (including efforts by the American Medical Association to stamp it out), and fortifies the chiropractic case with abundant statistics and close-knit argumentation.

Several historical scenes are reenacted, using actors in authentic costuming and settings. Production values are high, with Perkins appearing in beautiful natural settings or in strikingly lit interiors. The overall effect is warm, serious and engaging, though fast-paced. The narration, acting, graphic displays and music combine to create a sense of drama throughout the hour-long program.

A major message for consumers is not only that chiropractic has arrived but that individuals must take responsibility for their own good health, not leave those choices up to policymakers. When the third leading cause of death is malpractice, the health care system can no longer be accepted without question. "We vote with our feet," Perkins tells the viewers, encouraging that personal responsibility.

**Dr. Carl S. Cleveland, III, and his father, Dr. Carl Cleveland, Jr., arrive for their video interview**

**Dr. Virgil V. Strang, president of Palmer College, taping a segment of the documentary**

Here is Perkins' close:

*The future of health care comes down to philosophy. Sickness or wellness: Which philosophy makes the most sense? Your answer to that question affects the care you seek. Indeed, your answer determines what you'll insist upon as we continue to pursue health care reform in America. There is every evidence that the chiropractic profession will continue to lead the redefinition of health care – beginning from the philosophy of wellness.*

Four commercial spots were produced in conjunction with the documentary, featuring strong messages about the need for a wellness approach, the effectiveness of chiropractic care and the role of the nervous system in the body's natural healing ability. In one of the commercials, Dr. Terry Schroeder, captain of the U.S. Olympic water polo team, describes the success of chiropractic in caring for his teammates. Depending on their level of donation, chiropractors or chiropractic groups could purchase up to four of the spots for placement with a personalized advertising tag.

When the documentary and the commercials were shown in Washington and Davenport, the response was extremely enthusiastic. By mid-March 1996, $557,774.24 had been raised to purchase air time, much of it on the spot after the two gala preview showings. Expressions heard from dozens of people included "simply wonderful," "what we've needed for so long," "hard-hitting," "impressive logic," "brought tears to my eyes," and "will move our profession forward." Many doctors and chiropractic students reported favorable reaction from their patients once the documentary was shown on television. "It made so much sense," was a typical response.

Dr. William Holmberg, who, of course, described the documentary as "fantastic," said several months after the Centennial year was over that the documentary was the one CCF accomplishment he was most pleased about. "I had the dream of a major piece on television for many years," he said, "and I am just so happy we got the job done and that the final product was of such outstanding quality. The profession owes Guy (Riekeman) a lot for the T.L.C. he lavished on this project. We're going to keep arranging to show it as often as we can."

Dr. Virgil Strang, of Palmer College, said: "I don't know of any medium that has more power than television. If we could only handcuff the consumers to their chairs and force them to watch that documentary, we'd turn our image problem around in one hour."

**When chiropractors saw the documentary, they were willing to support its television airing**

**Television commercials were made available to the profession**

# Producing the documentary – talk about agony and ecstasy!

Of all the projects associated with the Centennial, none would be as daunting as the chiropractic documentary. It was high risk from the beginning, a political powderkeg with big money at stake, in the hundreds of thousands of dollars. Would it fly or flop?

Many in the profession agreed with the CCF that a documentary about chiropractic, well exposed on television, would have a positive impact on the profession's public image. After all the chiro-bashing on *"20/20"* and *"The Crusaders,"* as well as in the print media, wouldn't it be great to see the chiropractic side of things on big-time TV?

Others weren't so sure. What if it couldn't be placed except at 3 a.m. Saturday morning? What if the public didn't get the point? Would there really be the bang for the buck? Maybe the money should be spent elsewhere, perhaps on straight television advertising.

The documentary was a $400,000 gorilla, and it climbed on the back of one man, Dr. Guy Riekeman, of Colorado Springs, Colorado.

When he first got the invitation from Dr. Roger Hulsebus of the Centennial Board to head up media projects, Dr. Riekeman probably didn't realize what he was getting into. By the time the documentary was edited and ready for distribution, it had proved to be a major commitment, one that whipsawed him between exhilaration one minute and high anxiety the next.

Riekeman's work on the documentary reflected the reasons he got involved in the Centennial at all. "For one thing, I wanted to celebrate the people who pioneered in this profession, people like my father, who after 40 years in the profession had nobody to tell him

*"Finally, we wanted all facets of the profession to be fairly represented."*

thank you in an appropriate way. For another, our profession at this point in time is more paralyzed than ever, wondering how it will fit into managed care. I wanted to give chiropractors a sense of confidence that chiropractic has the very philosophy that today's consumer is demanding. Most importantly, I wanted to help consumers have greater confidence in what our profession has to offer."

The desire to persuade consumers would override everything else. The particular consumers the documentary would target would be those in the 25-49-age demographic, people with a relatively high standard of living who were independent enough to make their own health care decisions.

"There were several dimensions to the challenge," Riekeman said. "One was to represent an entire profession's historical development in under an hour. So much, including my own comments, by the way, ended up on the cutting room floor. Another was to produce this one hour commercial so that it didn't look like a commercial and do it without a controversial approach. Finally, we wanted all facets of the profession to be fairly represented."

A strong concept, but the execution didn't come easily. Flying around the country to interview difficult-to-schedule people on camera would broaden Riekeman's relationships with the movers and shakers of the profession he loves. It would also put him on the hot seat. "There was a need to play politics, and I have never considered myself much of a politician," he said.

He probably didn't change that evaluation in Washington. Editing under tight time constraints, Riekeman was unable to let the CCF planners and other key leaders preview the first version of the film. When they finally saw it, several were not happy. One influential chiropractor (not a CCF member) described its portrayal of the profession as "archaic." It would not be accepted in its present form. Finally, the National Chiropractic Mutual Insurance Company (NCMIC) came to the rescue, pitching in extra money to pay for a re-editing that would include comments from Deepak Chopra, George McAndrews and others.

That wasn't the only hitch. When the documentary was placed on television, some of the networks and stations rejected it for unspecified "reasons of content." In other cases, show times publicized by chiropractors and colleges were changed without notice by the networks. Some chiropractors had taken out advertisements. Others had office gatherings to watch

**Dr. Roger Hulsebus, right, invited Dr. Riekeman to join the Centennial planners**

the documentary only to see Richard Simmons lead weight-loss exercises. Angry phone calls followed to local stations and to the CCF office. Affiliates of CNBC inadvertently ran two brief commercial segments over part of the documentary when it aired on March 3.

Finally, things got squared away, and many chiropractors and chiropractic groups worked to place the film on local or regional cable stations. Even the initial chaotic nine-day period resulted in 31 airings, reaching an estimated 197,411,110 households. What had started out looking like a potential debacle ended up another Centennial success.

Riekeman attributed the eventual success of the airing to Stephen Eckstone, Ph.D., assistant to the president, Palmer College of Chiropractic West, who came on board the CCF media projects committee. Dr. Eckstone's media experience helped out in production as well as placement. "Without Steve the final product wouldn't have had the quality and style it had," Riekeman said.

The documentary would take an enormous amount of Riekeman's time and a toll on his private business. "It basically took me away from my business for a year," he said. "There was a six-week period when we were editing that I didn't go into the office even one day. I was a ghost figure in my own company. I kept reminding myself that this project was serving some greater purpose."

Not that it was a bad experience. He said it was heart-warming to see the love and generosity of Dr. William Harris, who offered a large challenge donation, and it was gratifying to see all the chiropractors who stepped forward to contribute for the airing. "The love people in this profession have for it rejuvenated me. And I'm very happy with the final product. I think it accomplishes that greater purpose."

**Raising money for the documentary was reminiscent of an old-time religious revival**

Stephen Eckstone, Ph.D.

# Harris challenge boosts documentary

Getting the money to air the chiropractic documentary owed much to one highly successful chiropractor, Dr. William Harris of Alpharetta, Georgia. Dr. Harris, who started the Foundation for the Advancement of Chiropractic Education, issued a sizable challenge donation to the profession.

Based on a cascading scale, beginning at 25 percent of the first $100,000 raised, Dr. Harris agreed to increase the percentage of the Foundation's contribution up to the point the profession collected $500,000. Along with Dr. Guy Riekeman, Dr. Harris, in his distinctive red cap, appeared at the showing of the documentary in both Washington, D.C., and Davenport, helping energize the crowd in a revival-style fund raising that eventually reached the $500,000 goal.

In urging the profession to support the documentary, Dr. Harris said: "Because of the sacrifices of our chiropractic pioneers, we are enjoying many benefits today. The documentary will be the first TV production telling the truth. It will be viewed in

**Dr. William Harris leads the charge**

major TV markets. Think of the exposure and what it will mean to attract new patients to you. ... All I have or ever hope to have I owe to chiropractic.

"On the plains of indecision bleach the bones of countless millions, who, on the dawn of victory – hesitated and while hesitating died. Act now, today! Don't give until it hurts – give until it feels GOOD!"

# One billion opportunities to hear about chiropractic!

Exactly how many would hear about the chiropractic Centennial will never be known, but the public relations people estimated that – at least by the time the documentary was aired – there would be a billion opportunities to hear the message.

Here's how they came up with that figure. Television, radio and newspaper people conduct surveys to find out how many households get the newspaper or have the television or radio tuned to a channel at a particular time. They multiply that figure by the average number of people in a household (usually using the figure 2.5) for their totals. They also have tracking methods, including clipping services, to determine which media actually carried certain stories or ran chiropractic advertisements.

Based on that calculation it was estimated that approximately 450 million people had an opportunity to see the Rose Parade float and hear a message of up to two minutes about chiropractic. An additional one million people watched along the parade route.

The Reynolds Communications Group, from Evanston, Illinois, one of two public relations agencies hired to spread the chiropractic message, estimated print impressions totaled 266,913,816, ranging from brief notes about chiropractic events to full-blown stories about the history of chiropractic. As a notable example of the latter, in November 1994 the *Chicago Sun-Times* ran a good-sized article, "Realigning an Image – Chiropractors Try to Straighten Out Misconceptions." The *Sun-Times* is read by half a million people daily.

The Reynolds report to the CCF board noted that clipping services only find 25 to 50 percent of stories actually printed. With that in mind, the firm believes "the number of impressions is far greater than (the nearly) 267 million."

## Here's how those print impressions were made throughout the Centennial year.

| | |
|---|---|
| Kickoff coverage (September 1994) | 25,380,000 |
| Fall/winter campaign | 18,392,962 |
| Rose Parade print coverage | 18,079,825 |
| Winter/spring campaign | 20,138,268 |
| Spring/summer campaign | 16,324,708 |
| Summer campaign | 9,182,288 |
| Summer/fall coverage | 159,415,765 |
| TOTAL | 266,913,816 |

Add the estimated 450,000,000 impressions from the Rose Parade TV coverage and the total is nearly 717 million impressions. Of course, there was no way of tracking how many chiropractic patients heard the Centennial message in their local chiropractor's office. Successful airing of the documentary would conceivably take care of the rest of the goal of one billion impressions.

Most of those impressions were not the result of media responding on their own to Centennial events but rather of concerted efforts by the CCF public relations firms, college public relations staffs, chiropractic associations and individual chiropractors to

*"… the most comprehensive public relations and advertising effort in the history of the profession."*

**Centennial year press coverage was something to celebrate**

generate publicity. Those efforts included sending out news releases, supplying pre-recorded radio interview messages, making personal and telephone pitches to editors and news directors, and supplying press kits.

Liz Meridian Lareau, public relations representative for Bawden & Associates, a Davenport advertising and public relations firm that handled most of the internal Centennial communications to the profession, estimated that her firm and the Reynolds Communications Group spent "probably about 5,000 man-hours in the effort." There is no way of knowing how much time was spent by all those actually involved in spreading the word.

Will what was called the "most comprehensive public relations and advertising effort in the history of the profession" be worth the money the CCF spent on it? Time will tell.

Mike Bawden, president of Bawden & Associates, noted: "A lot of the local chiropractors we worked with learned to be more confident dealing with the media, and a lot of doors were opened for the first time. I think the real impact of what everybody did will be determined by what the profession collectively and individually does from this point on. It was a tremendous public relations beginning and in itself a tremendous coming together by a fragmented profession. The question is where it will go from here."

## More than one way to skin a cat

Public relations efforts included making press kits available to local chiropractors and associations. Included in the kit were both news releases with photos and so-called matte releases, articles and photos laid out together and pre-printed for submission to community and weekly newspapers.

Stories submitted to the media included historical articles like "From One to 50,000: The Evolution of a Profession" and "1895-1995: A Century of Chiropractic Accomplishments." Other articles focused on carpal tunnel syndrome, choosing a chiropractor, workers' compensation and ergonomics,

"news you can use" features, debunking chiropractic myths, defining chiropractic terms, and comparing the roles of medical doctors, osteopaths and chiropractors.

Other approaches involved hometown radio spots and news releases, distributing brochures summarizing the Manga Report and other strategies. Much of the substance of the effort was educational, helping both the media and their viewers and readers not only become aware of Centennial events but, more importantly, understand what chiropractic is all about.

## OK, reporters, chew on these facts

A fact sheet called "Back Facts" distributed to the media contained much information to help offset unfavorable publicity that had dogged chiropractic up until the Centennial year. Here are a few of those items shared with the media.

- One in 15 Americans sees a chiropractor at least once a year.

- According to a 1990 study published in the *British Medical Journal*, chiropractic care is more effective for low-back pain than outpatient hospital care or many types of physical therapy.

- The annual cost of all chiropractic care in the United States is $2.4 billion, compared to $6 billion for AIDS and $4 billion for lung cancer.

- Chiropractic care is safer and more effective for back pain than medical approaches, says an

August 1993 study commissioned and funded by the Ontario Ministry of Health, and it could save the U.S. government millions of dollars every year.

- According to a 1991 Gallup poll, nine out of 10 chiropractic patients felt their treatment was effective, and eight out of 10 were satisfied with the care they received.

- When chiropractic care replaced traditional medical treatment for spine-related problems, workers' compensation costs and lost work time decreased by 50 percent, according to a 1988 Florida study.

- Chiropractors offer the lowest median cost per visit for therapeutic exercise, massage and ultrasound when compared to medical physicians, physical therapist and podiatrists, says a 1993 Virginia study.

# Chiropractic publicity turns into hardball

When CCF planners met with public relations professionals, the critical question was what should be publicized.

It was initially decided the most likely news interest would be in the Centennial itself, that trying to generate reporter interest in chiropractic care might be counterproductive in view of differences in chiropractic philosophy and practice, not to mention the spate of bad press prior to the chiropractic anniversary year.

However, the publication of the favorable low back care guideline from the Agency for Health Care Policy and Research changed the strategy. The timing was perfect for Centennial publicity, and many newspapers and electronic media jumped on the hook that chiropractic had gained a measure of acceptance after its century-long battle.

The press had a new storyline – not "unscientific quacks exploit public" but "chiropractic David overcomes medical Goliath." Several newspapers recounted the AMA conspiracy and chiropractic's victory in the Wilk case. Here's an example from the *Staten Island Register*. Reporter Barbara Naness wrote:

*It's been 100 years since the first chiropractic adjustment was performed on a patient, and it's been nearly two decades since the American Medical Association (AMA) began to recognize chiropractic as an acceptable way to treat certain kinds of pain.*

*It's about time people stopped viewing chiropractic as everything from "alternative" and "unconventional" to "new age" and even "quackery."*

*And apparently, many of them have.*

*Dr. Anthony Luciano, who has been practicing chiropractic in Oakwood Heights for 15 years, said he has seen "a complete turnaround" in the attitudes of both the public and the medical profession during that time.*

The story went on for a third of a journal-size page to recount the history of changing attitudes toward the profession, the stringent requirements for chiropractic education and licensure, and the increase in insurance coverage. The story was accompanied by a photograph of Dr. Luciano adjusting a patient.

Here's another example from Sedalia, Missouri. The headline and sub-headline read: "They've come a long way... And chiropractor J.W. Bryden doesn't plan for profession to take a back seat, ever again." Accompanied by a three-column photograph of Dr. Bryden looking at an x-ray, the story by reporter Larry Flower went like this:

*When Dr. J.W. Bryden began his chiropractic practice here in 1953, he was reluctant to tell a patient to take a drink of water lest he be accused of "practicing medicine."*

*In those days, the American Medical Association actively campaigned to brand chiropractors as quacks and Sedalia was hostile territory, Bryden said. But his apprehension – and frustration at being shut out of the health care community – turned to activism. Bryden was one of four chiropractors who won a federal anti-trust lawsuit against the AMA in 1987.*

*Times have changed. The chiropractic profession is "at its zenith" as it prepares to celebrate its 100th anniversary this September, Bryden said. ...*

However, the story noted the fight is not over and Dr. Bryden is likely to remain at the forefront. It outlined his role in the Wilk case and his continuing feistiness for the chiropractic cause.

*Bryden recalled an incident at his clinic earlier this year, when a woman patient was having difficulty standing and appeared disoriented. He told her she was suffering from an overdose of prescription medication. The woman provided him with a notarized letter detailing the medical doctor's response. The letter stated the doctor said the dosage he prescribed was correct and advised the patient "not to see the chiropractor any more."*

*"He doesn't know how to evaluate my practice," Bryden said. "I may hang him out to dry."*

Chiropractic publicity, anticipated as mostly soft-sell, turned into good ol' high-and-tight hardball.

> "It's about time people stopped viewing chiropractic as... quackery."

# Newspapers report unpaid testimonials

Many newspapers localized the Centennial story by finding area residents who had been helped by chiropractors, providing powerful unpaid testimonials to the efficacy of chiropractic.

Accompanied by a multi-column photograph of a chiropractor and a patient, an article distributed by *Gannett News Service* recounted the experience of Diane Minor, a satisfied chiropractic patient. Reporter Sue MacDonald wrote:

*Five years after a 1987 automobile accident, Diane Minor of Woodlawn, Ohio, still was having problems — lower back pain, muscle spasms, headaches, pain so severe she would break into sweats.*

*All that despite a constant stream of visits to doctors, bone specialists, soft-tissue experts and prescriptions for painkillers and muscle relaxant drugs.*

*What finally brought relief — and what a government panel recently recommended as the first line of treatment for lower back pain — was low-stress exercise, non-prescription pain medicine and a visit to a chiropractor.*

*Two years ago, Minor sought treatment from Dr. Tony Clasen, a chiropractor with Weis Chiropractic Health Center in Evendale, Ohio.*

*He taught Minor how to use her back at work and home, and exercises to keep her back, shoulder and leg muscles limber and strong. Clasen also performed spinal manipulation, realigning and adjusting the spinal column to keep it in balance. . . .*

*"I know some people question chiropractic services,"* said Minor, 41, a retail clerk. *"I thought, what could a chiropractor do if they don't treat you with medicine? But he helped me when I was at the end of my rope. If I hadn't gone to a chiropractor, I would probably be in traction now."*

A strongly pro-chiropractic story – with a large, dramatic graphic illustrating the role of the spine in various health disorders – appeared in the *Cedar Rapids Gazette* in Iowa. Here's the anecdote offered by free-lance writer Janet Brown:

*Deborah Schmitz, 42, of Ely, resisted going to a chiropractor for treatment of a severe abdominal problem until she had accrued more than $40,000 in medical bills.*

*For more than 18 months, she saw specialists, took medications and underwent surgery; but the daily pain and nausea persisted.*

*A nurse, she thinks she avoided chiropractic because of negative comments she heard as a medical professional.*

*"I feared I was going to hurt worse. They mess with your spine and I'd end up paralyzed," she says. But she was desperate. Finally, she was told by a doctor at an Iowa City hospital that he couldn't find anything wrong but that the problem might originate in her back.*

*Several months later, a friend suggested she see a chiropractor. Because Schmitz was afraid, the friend went with her on her first visit to Cedar Rapids chiropractor Dr. Douglas Dvorak.*

*Following a physical examination that included x-rays, he diagnosed a nerve irritation at the level of her spine that controls the stomach.*

*After manual adjustments by Dvorak over a two-week period, the daily pain and nausea were "all but gone." At the end of three weeks, all symptoms were gone and haven't returned in the four years since.*

*"What finally brought relief was... a visit to a chiropractor."*

## Scripps Howard describes chiropractic's acceptance

A widely circulated story by *Scripps Howard News Service* described chiropractic's history and explored AMA opposition.

One headline read: "Chiropractors Win Respect." An accompanying large type lead-in said: "For years, they were derided as quacks. They've been called unscientific, uneducated, unproven and dangerous. Organized medicine has tried to stamp them out. But as their profession nears its 100th anniversary, chiropractors find themselves cast in more flattering light."

Writer Greg Beaubien described the AMA boycott and the Wilk case, noting the possibility that the AMA's efforts represented an effort "to smash the competition."

Beaubien quoted Richard Dietzen, D.C., a Chicago chiropractor: "If anything, we're an economic threat. The AMA was pleased to try to distort the truth and make medical practitioners leery of us."

The writer also quoted James Winterstein, D.C., president of National College of Chiropractic, about the attitude of the medical profession since the victory in the Wilk case. "I think it (medical opposition) is now an informal thing. Organized medicine in large measure continues to express a bias against chiropractic."

Beaubien's story went on to describe the extensive education and training chiropractors receive. "Medical doctors – who are required to finish eight years of post-secondary training – might be surprised to know that chiropractic students take many of the same undergraduate courses, including anatomy, physiology and pathology, Dr. Winterstein says."

The story concluded: "Like medical doctors and dentists, chiropractors are licensed as physicians. The difference is that chiropractors aren't allowed to write prescriptions or perform surgery. But being non-surgical and drug-free is the whole idea behind chiropractic."

## Chiropractic for more than back pain

The Suburban Parent section of the Illinois newspaper *Winnetka Talk* explored the chiropractic alternative – not for back pain – but for ear infections and colic. The story by Kathie Mitchell described the experience of Amy Joffe, who took her son to Dr. Warren Bruhl, a Glencoe, Illinois, chiropractor, who helped her son, Dillon, get rid of recurrent ear infections without antibiotics.

*Dillon, who is now 19 months old, has been seeing Bruhl since July. "So far, he hasn't had another ear infection. He's had a couple of minor colds, which have not turned into ear infections," Joffe said. …*

*A subluxation, misalignment or improper movement of vertebrae, can cause pressure that creates drainage problems* in the ear, explained Bruhl. An adjustment can then help relieve that pressure and allow drainage. …

Citing FCER research studies on otitis media, colic and asthma, the article suggested that advancing knowledge would strengthen chiropractic's role, especially in cooperation with other health care disciplines.

*"We don't try to replace pediatricians," said Bruhl. "It's important to work with pediatricians to provide referrals and work as a team."*

The *Winnetka Talk* is hardly the *Wall Street Journal,* which before the Centennial had thrashed chiropractic over ear infections, but hey!

# Kansas City Star says chiropractic is ailing

Although news stories during the Centennial year were far and away favorable to the chiropractic profession, that wasn't so in every case. Perhaps the most negative story was by "medical writer" Alan Bavley of the *Kansas City Star*, who linked default on chiropractic student loans to perceived economic troubles for the profession.

*Many chiropractors say their profession – which is celebrating its centennial this year – is in deep economic trouble.*

*Much of the profession has failed to adapt to the dramatic nationwide shift to new cost-cutting health insurance plans, they say. And chiropractic has yet to disavow the dubious health claims that keep it from gaining the respect it needs to survive.*

*"What you are seeing is a profession that is literally imploding," warns Ron Slaughter of Houston, founder of the National Association for Chiropractic Medicine. "Chiropractors are going to end up on the fringe of health care."*

Bavley's story listed figures charting declines in chiropractor incomes and patient visits and laid the problem at the feet of managed care.

*Managed-care plans, designed to hold down costs, are rapidly taking over the health insurance market from traditional insurance. They save money by restricting access to medical specialists and by excluding services like chiropractic that aren't considered essential.*

*Typically, patients in a managed-care plan need a primary care physician's approval before seeing a specialist. This aspect of managed care has presented an enormous obstacle to chiropractors.*

*"Physicians have a very poor opinion of chiropractors, and when the managed-care networks were formed, they weren't friendly to them," said Glenn Meister of the Los Angeles office of A. Foster Higgins & Co., a national health benefits consulting firm. "Most of the large networks still do not include chiropractors."*

Bavley's story said Slaughter expects only about 15,000 of the 40,000 to 50,000 chiropractors now in practice to be integrated into mainstream medicine.

The writer did provide support for a more positive view by quoting Carl S. Cleveland III, D.C., president of the Cleveland Colleges of Chiropractic. Dr. Cleveland pointed out "about 80 percent of Americans will suffer lower-back pain at some point. And lower-back pain is second only to the common cold as a reason for missing work. Given the epidemic of lower-back pain, there's tremendous growth potential for the profession," he said.

The contrast between the Slaughter and Cleveland perspectives was dramatic.

*Slaughter said he has talked to more than 100 chiropractic school graduates in the last few years. He found that by the time they had been out of school for five years, two-thirds no longer were practicing.*

*A survey by Cleveland Chiropractic College of its December 1993 graduates found that one year out, 12 percent were not practicing.*

*Carl Cleveland sees the positive side.*

*Eighty-five plus percent are prospering, he said. "They are saving people from surgery. They are truly changing people's lives."*

The *Kansas City Star* wasn't the only paper to claim chiropractic is a declining profession. The *Rock Island Argus*, right next door to Davenport, a newspaper that generally gave positive Centennial coverage, dwelt on continuing medical skepticism about chiropractic excesses and recounted the plight of a recent Palmer College graduate who couldn't find a chiropractic job for nearly six months.

Again, the story wasn't entirely negative. It suggested "the pendulum may be starting to swing back for chiropractic" and quoted Peter Wundram, executive director of the Rock Island County and Scott County medical societies, who said many insurance companies are taking a new look at alternative treatments in cases where ailments do not respond to the treatment of physicians.

*"When the managed-care networks were formed, they weren't friendly to (chiropractors)."*

# Hospital privileges still tough to come by

Several newspaper articles described progress, or lack of it, that chiropractors are having in working with medical doctors through mutual referrals and in hospital settings.

A story in the *Poughkeepsie Journal* talked about Drs. Elliot and Mark Sussin, of Sussin Chiropractic in Rhinebeck, New York, who were opening a satellite office in Northern Dutchess Hospital's Center for Wellness and Rehabilitation.

The article noted that a recent survey of Dutchess County residents showed 45 percent of those responding used chiropractic services regularly and that 25 percent of physicians who responded to the survey said they have referred patients to chiropractors.

Another story distributed by *Scripps Howard News Service* discussed the hard fight chiropractors in Bloomington, Illinois, still have gaining acceptance in hospitals.

*Local chiropractors have been denied access to diagnostic equipment at local hospitals. In fact, about the only way chiropractic patients can get an MRI scan at a local hospital is to be referred to a medical doctor, who must order a test.*

*So in 1994, chiropractors leased a mobile MRI unit that now travels to a College Avenue parking lot periodically to conduct MRI scans, at a cost of about $1,000 each.*

*"It's not an ideal situation for us but we do get the information we need," said Dr. Steve Troyanovich, a chiropractor. ...*

About working with physicians Dr. Troyanovich had this anecdote:

*Dr. Troyanovich was even allowed into a Twin City hospital recently to visit one of his patients and consult with a surgeon. The patient came to him complaining of neck and back pain as a result of a car accident, for which he had been treated at an Indiana hospital. But after taking x-rays, he discovered the man had an undiagnosed spinal fracture and had him immediately transferred by ambulance to the hospital.*

# Ergonomics, carpal tunnel featured

Two news releases from the Reynolds Communications Group that received wide play across the country involved ergonomics and carpal tunnel syndrome.

The ergonomics story talked about the growing problem of on-the-job injuries, with special attention to low back pain. Of course, the important contribution of chiropractic was highlighted.

*As cases of lower back pain grow — 80 percent of Americans will suffer from back pain some time in life — chiropractic is becoming a primary means of treatment. In fact, nearly 20 million people are making the 100-year-old profession the nation's third largest health profession and the largest drug-free, non-invasive health care alternative.*

*The U.S. Department of Health and Human Services Agency for Health Care Policy and Research recently issued guidelines for those suffering from acute low back pain. The agency ranked spinal manipulation — usually performed by a chiropractor — among the most effective treatments during the first month of lower back pain symptoms.*

The article concluded by listing the telephone numbers of the American Chiropractic Association and the International Chiropractors Association to call for more information on how chiropractic can help treat workplace injuries.

The story on carpal tunnel syndrome identified the ailment as "the epidemic of the 1990s."

Carpal tunnel syndrome was a topic the media were interested in

Dr. Mark Davini, a Massachusetts chiropractor, was cited as an expert on carpal tunnel, encouraging people to receive the earliest evaluation possible. Exercises from Dr. Davini were listed, as well as the telephone numbers of the American Chiropractic Association and the International Chiropractors Association.

# Boosting chiropractic the indirect way

One approach in Centennial public relations was to inject chiropractic into the public consciousness indirectly through so-called "how-to stories." The Chiropractic Centennial Foundation was positioned as an adviser on practical health matters.

For instance, the CCF was cited as giving advice on improving posture. A column appearing in California newspapers had a tidbit called "MTV Generation, Beware." It noted a study from France that showed 70 percent of students who watch more than two hours of TV a day experienced back pain. The article went on to say:

*The average American child spends three hours a day in front of the tube. The strange positions they sit in while watching TV put their backs at risk of injury.*

*According to the study, back pain increased sharply after age 12. Sixty percent of females experienced back pain, compared to 43 percent of the males.*

*The Chiropractic Centennial Foundation recommends spending less time watching TV, sit up straight, stretch before participating in sports and carry books and bags in a backpack, rather than over one shoulder.*

Another example appeared in Illinois newspapers, this one on how to handle spring moving chores.

*During this season, apartment-dwellers move when leases run out, families move while younger children are out of school on break and parents help children move off of college campuses for the summer.*

*With all of this moving going on, people are more likely to run into back problems, said Dr. William Holmberg, president of the Chiropractic Centennial Foundation. It's easy to overdo it when lifting items that are too heavy for one person.*

*"For 100 years, chiropractors have specialized in caring for back pain and disorders of the spine," Holmberg said. "And spring moving season has traditionally been a big time for us. People often try to lift furniture and boxes that are much too heavy for one person."*

In other newspapers, the CCF was cited as the authority on how to shovel snow, chop wood, ice skate and ski.

# Celebrities provide good publicity hooks

There's a saying in journalism that people read about people and not about events. In that regard, the presence of celebrity participants in Centennial events provided opportunities for reader and viewer interest.

Actor Alan Thicke, who performed at the Centennial kickoff and the two galas, was featured in print and television. A television crew in Davenport also interviewed his sister, Dr. Joanne Thicke, a Brampton, Ontario, chiropractor.

**Alan Thicke and chiropractor-sister Dr. Joanne Thicke**

Stephen Covey, one of the nation's leading motivational speakers, also provided good copy. His book, *The 7 Habits of Highly Effective People*, was on the *New York Times* best seller list for almost four years.

Ray Charles, the featured attraction at the "Salute to the Palmer Family" in Davenport, received a favorable review. *Rock Island Argus* staff writer Sean Leary reported:

*Judging by the size of the crowd, you would have thought they were giving away money at The Mark of the Quad-Cities Thursday night.*

*Unfortunately for my wallet, they weren't. Instead, Ray Charles and a few area entertainers were out to help celebrate Palmer Chiropractic's 100th anniversary — and the shindig, attended by close to 11,000 well-dressed people, was a fitting jewel to mark such an occasion.*

Ethel A. Brindle, a retired chiropractor from Waynesboro, Pennsylvania, isn't a celebrity but she provided readership interest in another way. Her plans to attend the Washington gala were featured in a news article because Dr. Brindle was 98 years old. Her career spanned more than 60 years after her graduation from Palmer College in 1918.

Of course, she had to respond to the standard question, "To what do you attribute your longevity?" Her answer was what you expect. "Chiropractic has been the foundation of my good health."

**Centennial attendees included Dr. Ethel Brindle, 98**

# Pro-chiropractic columnist takes slap at postal system

Chiropractic has a friend in one columnist, who took a poke at the Canadian postal system for dragging its feet for seven years at providing a chiropractic commemorative stamp. The Canadian system finally came through with a stamp package of several designs, but before that happened a syndicated column by Arthur Black took the system to task. It appeared in the *Ingersoll Times* of Ingersoll, Ontario, and other newspapers.

*Seems the Canadian Chiropractic Association thought it might be nice to honor Doctor Daniel Palmer this year. Palmer was a Canadian who happened to found the chiropractic profession exactly 100 years ago. ...*

*Alas to no avail. Their petition to the stamp committee has come back marked "return to sender." Canada Post turned down the request.*

*However the corporation did find the will this year to issue several other commemorative stamps to honor the Monarch butterfly, a couple of cartoon characters and (for the third time) the Fortress of Louisbourg.*

*From what I can gather, my chiropractor friend takes all this personally, inferring that Canada Post's cold shoulder is discrimination against the chiropractic profession.*

*I think he's overreacting. I think Canada Post is just doing what it does best: Being Out of Touch. ...*

*But then the problem never was with posties – only with the huge, faceless, brain-dead bureaucracy that runs the place.*

*The men and women who actually handle our mail at Canada Post are as marvellous as, well, your average chiropractor. Maybe that's the problem between chiropractors and the Post Office bureaucracy right there. Different specialties.*

*Chiropractors mostly deal with lower back pain. Canada Post causes pain a little further down.*

Whether Black's column stimulated the postal system into producing the stamps is a matter of dispute. Maybe U.S. chiropractors should ask him to write a column about the U.S. postal service, which failed to approve a commemorative stamp in the country where chiropractic was founded.

**Canada honored the Chiropractic Centennial with a postage stamp, but the United States did not**

# Press notes boost to Q-C economy

Media coverage – both print and electronic – of the Centennial celebration in Davenport was thorough and positive, in part because of the boost to the Quad-City economy. *Rock Island Argus* reporter Leon Lagerstam's story included these comments:

*About 5,000 chiropractors are improving the economic health of the Quad-Cities by attending the largest convention ever held here, a Quad Cities Convention & Visitors Bureau spokesperson said Thursday.*

*Teri Wonderlich, bureau director of sales and marketing, said it's exciting how the Quad-Cities community is "embracing the convention." Ms. Wonderlich said the event's success hopefully "will bring more large events to town."*

*The bureau estimates that each of the 5,000 chiropractors and chiropractic supporters in town through Saturday will spend an average of $125 every day to generate $2.5 million of tourism dollars.*

*It also is estimated that another $7.8 million will be raised indirectly when money spent by visitors for lodging, restaurants, transportation, shopping and entertainment gets passed on multiple times by residents of the Quad-Cities.*

*Totally, the convention is expected to produce $10 million of economic impact, but Ms. Wonderlich said that (figure) actually may be a low estimate "because you're bringing in a group of doctors who may be able to spend more than we're estimating."*

*More than $438,000 was spent by the Chiropractic Centennial Foundation to rent the RiverCenter, hire local workers and food vendors, pay for a MetroLink shuttle service and for a variety of other convention supplies, according to Liz Meridian Lareau, a public relations liaison for the foundation.*

**Downtown Davenport was humming, and the media took notice**

**Restaurants were happy about the increased business**

**Davenport's new RiverCenter exhibition hall was a principal site of the chiropractic gala**

# Ad supplements boost chiropractic

Newspapers with circulation over 20,000 in the 65 largest metropolitan areas were invited to participate in an eight- to 12-page tabloid-size advertising supplement about chiropractic.

In many cases, the CCF provided the editorial content (or worked with newspaper writers) while the paper's sales staff sold the remaining space to local chiropractors and others who wanted to advertise in the publication. The supplement in the *Quad-City Times* in Davenport included not only ads from chiropractors but also from Hawkeye Medical Supply, Inc., offering "supplies for the doctor, hospital, student and the home."

Editorial content included stories on the Centennial celebration, the history of chiropractic, the advantages of chiropractic for back care, and the respective roles of chiropractors, medical doctors and osteopaths.

A large advertising supplement in the *Des Moines Sunday Register* contained other interesting features, including what people can do to secure chiropractic care through legislative action, a quiz to test reader knowledge of chiropractic, what to expect at your first visit to a chiropractor, and an extensive summary of studies supporting chiropractic. They included not only the Manga report but also a Florida workers compensation study, one by the Robins School of Business, one from the University of Richmond, the Rand study, a Washington HMO study, a Utah workers compensation study, the 1990 *British Medical Journal* report and the Gonyea report.

**Ad supplements helped the chiropractic cause**

# MD columnist praises chiropractors

The praise for chiropractic from a few newspaper columnists was remarkable. Consider these comments from Kent DeLong, M.D. Dr. DeLong is an internal medicine physician with the Beaver Medical Clinic in Banning, California. His syndicated column ran February 5, 1995, in the San Bernardino, California, *Sun* under the headline: "Chiropractors sometimes get better results than M.D.s."

*If many M.Ds still have difficulty understanding what a chiropractor does, there are few who couldn't give stories of patients helped by chiropractic techniques. ...*

*A 1991 Rand Corporation study endorsed spinal manipulation for low back pain.*

*Another published in the* Western Journal of Medicine *reported that patients of chiropractic physicians were three times more likely to be helped than if they received traditional treatments from their family physician.*

*These kinds of studies are appearing throughout the medical literature and they clearly can't be ignored, nor are they.*

*The federal Agency for Health Care Policy and Research recently released guidelines for the management of lower back pain which include spinal manipulation within the first month of symptoms.*

*Even managed care organizations are seeing the benefits of improved patient care using chiropractic techniques.*

*In fact, chiropractic care was a covered benefit for over 50 percent of all HMO patients at the end of 1994. As recently as 1992, fewer than a quarter of HMO patients were offered this benefit. ...*

*And with the level of patient satisfaction that exists with chiropractic care, this growth will continue well into the next century.*

# Local chiropractors reap the benefits

Many chiropractors received favorable publicity as they were cited as examples of chiropractic's success. For example, a father and son chiropractic team, Drs. Peter and Darin Berardi, were featured in the Fairfield, California, *Daily Republic*.

The Beradis, along with Dr. Gerard Clum, president of Life College of Chiropractic West, were quoted for their views on chiropractic's degree of acceptance. The story by reporter Amy Maginnis concluded with an anecdote about a satisfied patient, John Taylor.

*Twenty years ago he ended up in what was then Intercommunity Hospital's emergency room with severe chest pain.*

*The doctor diagnosed a pinched nerve in his back and offered Taylor pain pills, explaining that the pain would do one of three things – improve, worsen or stay the same.*

*"That was treating the symptom not the cause," Taylor said.*

*The next day Peter Berardi adjusted his back.*
*"I can't describe how fast I felt relief," Taylor said.*
*"It was almost instantly that the pain went away."*

*During the past two decades, Taylor has sought Berardi for various spinal and skeletal problems.*

*He named three main reasons for continuing chiropractic care:*

- *"It works," he said. "The true test of any healing art is how well it works."*
- *It works without being invasive.*
- *It's patient-centered. "It's about the ability of human beings to heal themselves."*

# Air play from Minneapolis to Beeville

One of the grassroots public relations approaches conceived and implemented by the Reynolds Communications Group with outstanding success involved radio interviews with local chiropractors. Reynolds placed the pre-recorded messages about the Centennial with the doctors' hometown radio stations.

The radio spots, offered free to the stations, were not only used extensively but produced and distributed at a tiny fraction of the cost of radio advertising. One month after the September kickoff, 172 acceptances were reported, including two national and seven regional networks representing 1,137 total stations. Stations running the spots ranged from those in sizable cities like Minneapolis, Minnesota, and Nashville, Tennessee, to small towns like Yermo, California, and Beeville, Texas.

The total estimated audience for the interviews was 24,300,400 as of the agency's usage report dated October 27, 1994. Audience figures were listed for each station as reported by the stations, Arbitron and the Bureau of Broadcast Measurement for Canadian Stations.

Using a one-time average spot rate of $100 per minute for each station and each airing (average two per station), the equivalent advertising expenditure would have been $120,600. The cost to reach 24,300,400 listeners through this public relations tactic was $.41 per thousand. In comparison, the cost to reach 24 million-plus listeners through purchased advertising time would have been $4.96 per thousand, Reynolds said.

# TV coverage in Davenport is extensive, favorable

The Centennial climax in Davenport brought a flurry of favorable television coverage from local stations, commenting on the economic impact and providing information about the history, acceptance and future of the profession.

One television station, KWQC (Channel 6), showed the impact of the celebration in various ways – golf courses that had all they could handle, restaurants bustling with business and the reaction of visitors to the Quad-City area. A sound bite featured a Norwegian chiropractic student who indicated nearly half his country's chiropractors would be coming to Davenport. Chiropractic visitors and students, faculty and administrators from Palmer College were frequently on the noon, evening and 10 o'clock news.

The most thoughtful coverage was on WQPT (Channel 12), a public television station. One entire "Perspective" show discussed chiropractic with factual and hard-hitting information from William Meeker, D.C., director of research for Palmer College and Palmer College West; Jerry McAndrews, D.C., of the American Chiropractic Association; and Don Betz, Ph.D., provost and vice president of academic affairs for Palmer College.

Dr. McAndrews laid out for viewers a clear picture of how the AMA's 31-year boycott, "which was not really over until 1992," tainted the fabric of society with false impressions about chiropractic. He explained that restricted Medicare insurance coverage, wherein x-rays are not reimbursed, was a product

Dr. William F. Holmberg
spent a lot of time in
front of microphones
during the Centennial year

104

of the boycott and expressed hope such inequities would eventually be addressed.

Dr. McAndrews attacked a common misperception that chiropractors require unlimited visits that end up costing more than visits to physicians. He referred to studies that show visits to medical doctors cost twice as much per visit but visits to chiropractors are more frequent, bringing the totals for the respective experiences to comparable amounts. However, none of those studies adds in the cost of a related prescription or the cost of hospital referral for possibly unnecessary surgery. When all is said and done, McAndrews argued, "visits to chiropractors end up being half as expensive and twice as effective."

Dr. Meeker described the escalation of chiropractic research, especially since the 1970s, and showed its increasingly positive effect on health care policy. He predicted that the next 100 years would bring an explosion of scientific activity and continue to break down barriers between health care disciplines.

Dr. Betz outlined the world impact of chiropractic, noting that many emerging nations were turning to chiropractic for less expensive health care.

**The media showed up repeatedly at Centennial events in Davenport**

Dr. Jerry McAndrews

Dr. William Meeker

Dr. Don Betz

# Congress acknowledges chiropractic acceptance

Evidently for the first time in history proclamations commending chiropractic were read in both the United States Senate and House of Representatives, and made part of the *Congressional Record.*

Thanks to Jeanne Greenawalt, wife of Foot Levelers founder Monte Greenawalt, D.C., national and state legislators from Nevada, the Greenawalts' home state, produced and read four proclamations commending chiropractic in connection with the Centennial. Other proclamations were issued by various governmental executives and bodies throughout the country.

Mrs. Greenawalt reported that U.S. Senator Richard Bryan (D-Nevada) read the pro-chiropractic proclamation in the Senate, and U.S. Congressman John Ensign (R-Nevada) read a similar one in the House. Nevada state legislators also were supportive – Nevada State Assembly woman Chris Guinchigliani was responsible for a proclamation read on the floor of the Nevada state legislature, and Clark County Commissioner Erin Kenny drafted a proclamation presented at a gala celebration held in March by the Nevada State Chiropractic Association.

The event, held at the Greenawalts' Las Vegas home, was attended by leaders of 13 chiropractic colleges.

"I feel that we've helped legislative leaders realize that chiropractic is celebrating its Centennial and has an important place in the current health care system and any future health care plan," Mrs. Greenawalt said.

The *Congressional Record* now records historic facts about chiropractic such as these included in a statement in the record of the House of Representatives submitted by the Honorable George P. Radanovich of California:

• *Chiropractic is a science, a knowledge of health and disease reduced to law and embodied into a system.*

• *Chiropractic education is recognized by the Federal and State governments. The Commission on Accreditation of the Council on Chiropractic Education (C.C.E.) is recognized by the United States Department (Office) of Education and by the Council on Postsecondary Accreditation.*

• *Student aid programs for chiropractic students demonstrate that the Federal and State governments not only encourage education for chiropractic students but establish ways to finance that education.*

*"The chiropractic profession has an effective and valuable health care service to render humanity."*

• *Chiropractors are licensed in all fifty states, U.S. Virgin Islands, Puerto Rico and the District of Colombia, by an Act of the United States Congress. Chiropractors must meet the individual State requirements and pass a State Board examination for licensure.*

• *Chiropractors must meet the educational requirements and pass a State examination for certification for the supervision and use of radiation and x-ray machines.*

• *Chiropractors are accepted as expert witnesses within the lawful scope of the limited specialty of their practice in the County, State and Federal Court system.*

• *The Congress of the United States, with Presidential approval, has authorized the provision of chiropractic services under federal law for all Americans in Medicare and Medicaid. Federal employees have chiropractic coverage in the Federal Employee Health Benefits Program and coverage in the Federal Employee Workers' Compensation program, and in leave approvals, for illness suffered by federal employees. Chiropractic health services are included in the Railroad Retirement Act, State MediCal (Medicaid) program, State Workers' Compensation Insurance program and virtually all insurance carriers in the United States provide policies covering chiropractic care. Chiropractors perform disability evaluation for the courts and workers' compensation insurance programs. Chiropractors perform physical examination for school children and employment and insurance companies.*

• *Chiropractors are entitled to hospital staff membership by the Joint Commission on Accreditation of Hospitals (JCAH).*

• *The chiropractic profession has an effective and valuable health care service to render humanity.*

Copies of proclamations from the following states were received for the CCF archives: Alaska, Arkansas, California, Connecticut, Florida, Illinois, Iowa, Kansas, Louisiana, Massachusetts, Michigan, Mississippi, Missouri, Ohio, New Jersey, North Dakota, Oregon, Pennsylvania, South Carolina, South Dakota, Tennessee and West Virginia.

**THE GOVERNOR OF THE STATE OF FLORIDA**

**LAWTON CHILES**

### THE CENTENNIAL OF CHIROPRACTIC

WHEREAS, the chiropractic profession was founded on September 18, 1895, by Daniel David Palmer in Davenport, Iowa, in the United States America, and will therefore celebrate its centennial on September 18, 1995; and

WHEREAS, the profession of chiropractic is now practiced by doctors of chiropractic throughout the world, including 50,000 in the United States; and

WHEREAS, contemporary standards in chiropractic education, research and practice have led to ever broadening acceptance of the benefits of chiropractic health care by the public and the health care community; and

WHEREAS, each year millions of Americans now choose chiropractic health care for the restoration and maintenance of their health by natural methods and without the use of drugs or surgery;

NOW, THEREFORE, I, Lawton Chiles, Governor of the State of Florida, officially acknowledge the 100th anniversary of the founding of the chiropractic profession and the significant contribution that chiropractic has made to the health and welfare of Americans.

IN WITNESS WHEREOF, I have hereunto set my hand and caused the Great Seal of the State of Florida to be affixed at Tallahassee, the Capital, this 19th day of December in the year of our Lord nineteen hundred and ninety-four.

*Lawton Chiles*
GOVERNOR

A RECYCLED PAPER PRODUCT PRINTED WITH SOY INK

---

## STATE OF ALASKA

### Executive Proclamation
*by*
#### Walter J. Hickel, Governor

The Chiropractic profession was founded on September 18, 1895 by Daniel David Palmer in Davenport, Iowa in the United States of America, and will therefore celebrate its Centennial on September 18, 1995.

The profession of Chiropractic is now practiced by Doctors of Chiropractic throughout the world, including 50,000 in the United States.

Contemporary standards in Chiropractic education, research and practice have led to ever broadening acceptance of the benefits of Chiropractic health care by the public, and by the health care community.

Each year millions of Americans choose Chiropractic health care for the restoration and maintenance of their health by natural methods, and without the use of surgery or drugs.

NOW, THEREFORE, I, Walter J. Hickel, Governor of the State of Alaska, do acknowledge the:

### 100th ANNIVERSARY OF THE FOUNDING OF THE CHIROPRACTIC PROFESSION

and encourage all Alaskans to recognize the significant contributions that the Chiropractic profession has made to the health and welfare of Americans.

DATED: September 18, 1994

Done by ___

*Walter J. Hickel*
Walter J. Hickel, Governor
who has also authorized the seal
of the State of Alaska
to be affixed to this proclamation.

---

## The Commonwealth of Massachusetts

### A Proclamation
By His Excellency
GOVERNOR WILLIAM F. WELD
1995

WHEREAS: The chiropractic profession is commemorating 100 years of service to the citizens of the Commonwealth and the nation; and

WHEREAS: On September 18, 1895, the chiropractic profession was founded by Daniel David Palmer in Davenport, Iowa; and

WHEREAS: The chiropractic profession is practiced by doctors of chiropractic throughout the world, including 50,000 in the United States; and

WHEREAS: Contemporary standards in chiropractic education, research, and practice have led to a better understanding of the chiropractic profession by the health care community and the general public; and

WHEREAS: Each year, millions of people choose chiropractic health care to ensure their well-being;

NOW, THEREFORE, I, WILLIAM F. WELD, Governor of the Commonwealth of Massachusetts, do hereby honor and commend

### THE CHIROPRACTIC PROFESSION

on the occasion of its One Hundredth Anniversary

and urge all the citizens of the Commonwealth to take cognizance of this event and participate fittingly in its observance.

Given at the Executive Chamber in Boston, this twenty-third day of February, in the year of our Lord one thousand nine hundred and ninety-five, and of the Independence of the United States of America, the two hundred and nineteenth.

*William F. Weld*
WILLIAM F. WELD

By His Excellency the Governor

*William F. Galvin*
WILLIAM F. GALVIN
Secretary of the Commonwealth

GOD SAVE THE COMMONWEALTH OF MASSACHUSETTS

---

## Certificate of Recognition

*State of Iowa*
*State Senate*

To: Palmer College of Chiropractic
Davenport, Iowa

FOR: 100th Anniversary of the founding of the Chiropractic Profession.

WITNESS OUR HANDS, this 24th day of March, 1995

*Wally E. Horn*
Senate Majority Leader

*Leonard L. Boswell*
President of the Senate

*Jack Rife*
Senate Minority Leader

*Maggie Tinsman*
State Senator

*Patrick J. Deluhery*

**Many states saluted the Centennial with proclamations**

107

# The Historical Symposium in Davenport

*It was a rockin' revival of the old-time chiropractic spirit that had even the profession's liberals proclaiming that Innate was alive and well in Davenport. Unlike the case in Washington, attendance was strong, and despite some glitches, the grand finale left the participants in a warm glow. They would return to their homes with renewed confidence and pride.*

*"... the river will never dry for chiropractic provided it knows its way back to D.D. Palmer. ..."*

## Gala highlights Palmers' matchless contribution

Appropriately, the first session of the historical symposium in Davenport highlighted the contributions of D.D., B.J. and David Palmer, who played such critical roles in the development of the profession and chiropractic education. Three speakers with intimate knowledge of their subjects addressed a packed Adler Theatre audience.

Pierre-Louis Gaucher-Peslherbe, D.C., Ph.D., an eminent chiropractic historian, described D.D. Palmer as a man who had been largely neglected even in chiropractic literature. Dr. Gaucher said that, although D.D. had been written off as an overbearing man and generally much maligned, upon examination he has proved to be very well-educated, although not formally so, and a leading-edge thinker given the state of science in his era. For example, Palmer had a clear understanding of the application of biomechanical principles. "D.D.'s scientific knowledge was impressive and exacting and deserving of respect," Gaucher said.

Gaucher also referred to Palmer's philosophical and religious background. "Although it would be far too simplistic to suggest that the emergence of chiropractic was solely due to religious and/or spiritual factors, it would be perverse to overlook any connection between the two." Gaucher expressed hope for the future of chiropractic: "It is my deep conviction that the river will never dry for chiropractic provided it knows its way back to a constant awareness of D.D. Palmer's definition of the art."

Dr. Gaucher-Peslherbe

Davenport's RiverCenter was the hub for the Davenport gala, which featured history presentations like the one from Dr. W. Heath Quigley (inset)

Next, W. Heath Quigley, D.C., described B.J. Palmer as a glittering gem, presenting a different facet to every viewer. Dr. Quigley told of some of B.J.'s difficulties with his father, whom he admired and often tried to please without much success, and his fall from a position of professional dominance over the neurocalometer. Interestingly, Dr. Quigley noted that a tendency in B.J.'s thinking was to reduce ideas to their simplest expression. This "reductionistic" way of looking at things led B.J. to narrow chiropractic from the "300 articulations of the human skeletal frame," which he included in one of his

for his profession, he was not the autocratic man his chiropractic antagonists thought him to be. In the field of broadcasting he earned the respect and affection of his associates. ... The essential principle he advocated in his book *Radio Salesmanship* was that the elimination of unnecessary words made room for more essential words 'to sell more product.' It was a good example of his reductionism at its best and most productive level," Quigley said.

The presentation by Virgil V. Strang, D.C., the seventh president of Palmer College of Chiropractic, described "David Palmer's place in history as a

Dr. D.D. Palmer

Dr. B.J. Palmer

Dr. David D. Palmer

early definitions, down to the 24 vertebrae of the spine and eventually to two points of the upper cervical spine. "It is apparent that there was an obsessive need in B.J.'s efforts to reduce and simplify. He often finished a lecture in classes or in speeches in which he took great satisfaction and pleasure in ending with a signature summary, "It's as simple as that."

A departure from B.J.'s tendency to dominate was his involvement with radio broadcasting where he displayed "a different personality," one of an innovator rather than self-appointed leader. "When B.J. stepped outside his role of the chiropractic authority and was freed from his self-assumed responsibility

neglected topic. While D.D., B.J. and even Mabel Palmer have been consistently lauded and even idolized, David Palmer, in my view, has been given short shrift despite the enormous contribution he made to the profession and to chiropractic education."

Dr. Strang listed nine aspects of "Dr. Dave's" contribution: improved civic relationships, efforts toward professional and trade association unity, work toward accreditation, upgrading the Palmer faculty, toughening entrance requirements, taking Palmer to a non-profit 501(c)(3) institution, creation of a board of trustees, fostering the PCC International Alumni Association and expanding Palmer College facilities.

David Palmer's contributions empowered others to expand and refine chiropractic education, and his accomplishments hold a lesson for the profession, Strang said. "Can we successfully manage 21st century dynamics? Can we develop our interpersonal skills to the level of our clinical skills? Can we put principles for the greater good ahead of short-term gains for ourselves? Can we build more bridges and make less war? May each of us individually and our profession collectively take a good lesson from Dr. Dave."

Dr. Virgil V. Strang

# Chiropractic growth like a "high-wire act"

Those who attended the history sessions came away with a better understanding of forces that brought chiropractic to its present stage. Most of the presentations were in three sections – "Survival and Growth," "Dissension and Consolidation," and "Reform and Acceptance."

"History: Survival and Growth" included a presentation by William Rehm, D.C., who described the "Kansas Coconuts," hard-nosed Kansas chiropractors whose persistence brought legal victories in that state. Dr. Rehm traced the Kansas history of court and legislative battles, pointing to the chiropractors as examples of the ability to advance the profession in an orderly way.

Meridel Gatterman, D.C., provided a broad-brush description of chiropractic's growth from D.D. Palmer's day through the first third of the 20th century. She described the proliferation then contraction of chiropractic colleges and the impact of basic science laws (from which chiropractic ultimately benefited) as well as improved standards in chiropractic education.

The audience seemed especially attentive to Steven Martin, who brought an M.D.'s perspective to chiropractic history. His thesis: Chiropractic survived because of flexibility in reacting to social forces.

To the idea chiropractic's 100-year survival proves it works, Dr. Martin said, "Efficacy does not necessarily indicate whether a health care procedure survives," and he offered medical examples as evidence. Reaction to cultural and social factors ultimately determined chiropractic's success, he insisted. "As the context has changed, chiropractic has changed." For instance, chiropractic rode a wave of reaction against technology, seen as threatening the stable order. Chiropractic drew support from populism, appealing to the craft model at odds with the more technical, professional model. Yet, as the technical gained ground, B.J. Palmer and others were able to adapt. A key factor in chiropractic's adaptation was effecting legislation that defined chiropractic as a philosophy, art and science distinct from orthodox medicine.

In short, chiropractic has followed a parallel course to medicine, neither getting too close nor pulling too far away. Martin described it as a "high-wire act" facing new challenges under managed care.

In "History: Dissension and Consolidation," Dr. Carl S. Cleveland, III, explored the straight-mixer controversy, noting that the entire history of chiropractic is one of divergence and dissent. "Even B.J. was a dissenter from his father's original teaching, reducing the adjustment of 300 articulations down to the atlas." Dr. Cleveland applauded the Council on Chiropractic Education as providing unity and stability to the profession. "It is the only group that forces all the elements to the table at least once a year. It allows for diversity but brings unity. ... That's progress."

Historian Russell W. Gibbons described the AMA's vitriolic attack on chiropractic, focusing on Morris Fishbine and the "denial syndrome" that fueled the medical profession's dismissal of chiropractic. Gibbons also observed that scientists, historians and sociologists have been largely indifferent to the unfair treatment of chiropractic, a situation crying out for correction. He closed by referring to the songs "Strong Hearted Men" and "We Shall Overcome" as symbolizing what chiropractors were and did.

Dr. William Rehm   Dr. Meridel Gatterman

Stuart Moore, Ph.D., focused on the fall of B.J. Palmer as the profession's leader, a decline accelerated by the "neurocalometer debacle." B.J.'s response to those who disagreed about the merits of the device or who refused to comply with the expensive leasing agreement was anything but sincerely conciliatory. "B.J. threatened reprisal against those he called spittle lickers and blood suckers." In the end, Moore said, "B.J. had abused his authority, the magic of lyceum was gone, and the neurocalometer had turned into a neurocalamity."

In "History: Reform and Acceptance," Walter Wolf, D.C., discussed the history of accreditation of chiropractic, a protracted process in which he himself played a significant role. He was honored at the end of the session with the Lee Homewood Award for his contributions.

Mary-Anne Chance, D.C., outlined how chiropractic had been exported around the world. The progress worldwide has been steady, though uneven. Legislation, professional standards and educational requirements are factors. In many underdeveloped countries chiropractic care is available only to the relatively affluent. Dr. Chance portrayed the profession's ability to extend care to the majority who cannot afford it as "a test of our ingenuity and sincerity as humanitarians."

Walter Wardwell, Ph.D., one of the first non-chiropractor scholars to write about the historical treatment

*"As the context has changed, chiropractic has changed."*

of the profession and give chiropractic its due, explored future possibilities. Wardwell discounted the likelihood chiropractic would either be swallowed up by the medical profession or reduced to an ancillary position controlled by medical physicians. Nor did he see either medicine or physical therapy taking over chiropractic's role in spinal adjusting. Instead he predicted chiropractic would find a mainstream role – indeed, in many ways chiropractic already fits that model – as a "limited medical profession" like dentistry, podiatry, psychiatry and others.

To be fully accepted in the mainstream, chiropractic must pursue knowledge in common with medical professionals, and upgrade itself organizationally, including curtailing unethical advertising and practice-builders. "Chiropractic has had a successful past and can look forward to a glorious future," Wardwell concluded.

Other history presentations were organized by country or world region. Countries discussed included Australia, New Zealand, Japan, Denmark, France, Italy, Norway, United Kingdom, Brazil, Ecuador, Mexico, Panama, Greece, Iran and South Africa. Other original history research papers were presented in additional sessions.

Dr. Carl S. Cleveland, III

Russell Gibbons

Dr. Walter Wardwell

# History researchers shed more light

The following history platform presentations were delivered at the original research sessions at the Davenport gala.

**Early Controversies**, moderated by Russell W. Gibbons, B.A., F.I.C.A.: "Daniel David Palmer's Medical Library," Pierre Louis Gaucher-Peslherbe, D.C., Ph.D., Litt.D.; "Heat by Nerves and Not by Blood: The First Major Reduction in Chiropractic Theory, 1903," Joseph C. Keating, Ph.D.; "History of the Concept of Subluxation," Charles A. Lantz, D.C., Ph.D.; "Chiropractic's Tension with the Germ Theory of Disease," Glenda Wiese, M.A.

**Legacy of the Pioneers**, moderated by Glenda Wiese, M.A.: "The Evolution of Chiropractic Technique and Analysis," Robert Cooperstein, M.A., D.C.; "The Making of a European Chiropractor in the 1920's: Fred Illi and the Universal Chiropractic College," Pierre Louis Gaucher-Peslherbe, D.C., Ph.D., Litt.D.; "William C. Schultz, M.D., D.C. (1890-1936): From Mail-Order Mechano-Therapists to Scholarship and Professionalism Among Drugless Physicians," Joseph C. Keating, Ph.D.; "Dr. Arthur E. Lundh: The First D.C. in Norway," Kyrre Myhrvold, D.C.; "Cleveland Chiropractic: The Early Years, 1917-1933," Joseph C. Keating, Ph.D.

**Technique Wars**, moderated by William Rehm, D.C.: "Did Osteopathy 'Borrow' the Chiropractic Short Lever Adjustment (the Core of All Modern Manipulative Techniques) Without Giving Palmer Credit?" James W. Brantingham, D.C.; "Raymond Nimmo and the Evolution of Trigger-Point and Receptor-Tonus, 1929-86," Jeffrey Cohen, D.C.; "Diversified Chiropractic Technique, Historically Considered: Core of Chiropractic or 'Just Another Technique System'?" Robert Cooperstein, M.A., D.C.; "Unveiling an Enigma: The Origins and Development of Diversified Chiropractic Technique," Bart N. Green, D.C., C.C.S.P.; "The Legacy of a Chiropractor, Inventor and Researcher: Dr. Major Bertrand DeJarnette," Joseph F. Under, Jr., D.C., D.I.C.S.

**Struggle and Strife**, moderated by John Willis, D.C.: "Chiropractic in Ohio," Alana Callender, M.S.; "Morris Fishbein, M.D.: The 'Medical Mussolini' and Chiropractic," Joseph H. Donahue, D.C.; "The History of New York Chiropractic College: An American Tale," Mark H. Feldman, D.C., C.C.S.P.; "Why We Chiropractors Are in Jail," John F. Grone, D.C.; "Research and Science in the First Half of the Chiropractic Century," Joseph C. Keating, Ph.D.

**Breaking the Barriers**, moderated by Alana Callender, M.S.: "Chiropractic History: A Curriculum Necessity," Bart N. Green, D.C., C.C.S.P.; "Joshua N. Haldeman, D.C., The Canadian Years: 1926-1950," Joseph C. Keating, Ph.D.; "Chiropractic Pioneers in South Carolina," Edward J. McGinnis, D.C., F.I.C.C.; "An Australian Perspective on Chiropractic Spinography," Rolf E. Peters, B.Sc., D.C., F.I.C.C.; "The Evolution of the American Board of Chiropractic Orthopedists: A Bootstrapping of Clinical Skills."

# Philosophy speakers call for solidifying profession

The several Davenport philosophy sessions offered an eclectic mix of personal anecdotes, emotional expressions about chiropractic's efficacy, and argumentation about the meaning of philosophy and its appropriate role. Predictably, the sessions revealed the philosophy gap that continues to bedevil the profession.

The first session at the Adler Theatre featured Fred Barge, D.C., and Sid Williams, D.C., who energized the crowd with strong assertions about the continuing value of the big idea of chiropractic.

Dr. Barge told the crowd that, if they wanted "unlimited horizons for the next one hundred years, then we must go back to our non-therapeutic past." He predicted "the germ theory will go the way of the dodo bird in the next century." He urged the chiropractors not "to limit or constipate yourselves by taking the leavings from the back door of medical doctors," citing a figure of "80,000 deaths today from medical negligence in hospitals."

He also observed that current publicity in non-chiropractic quarters about psychoneuroimmunology, "love medicine" and miracles is corroborative of B.J. Palmer's emphasis on becoming attuned to Innate. Innate, which science will never be able to fully investigate, can be a source of revelation to the profession as well as to the individual. "Let us bring to the next generation the same power that originated the profession," Barge urged.

Amid rhythmic clapping and cheering, Dr. Williams came on stage intent on rousing the audience to "celebrate our own liberation and freedom." He encouraged them, "Don't be so ashamed of yourself that you can't exuberate," then led them in shouting, "I feel healthy, I feel happy, I feel terrific!"

As he had in Washington, Williams related his personal experience with chiropractic and what led up to his embracing the big idea – "bigger than religion, bigger than law, bigger than medicine, bigger than any I've known." Yet, the big idea of the chiropractic adjustment can be lost, he warned, and today's profession is in danger of losing it by "adopting a medical curriculum." He urged the crowds to put their faith not in medicine but in "the whole scheme of life. Do you have faith in the pill or in the power that made it, that activates the world?" He implored them to cling tenaciously to the chiropractic principles held by early chiropractic believers.

Gerard Clum, D.C., and James Winterstein, D.C., brought their point-counterpoint argument articulated in Washington to the next philosophy session, each making strong cases from their differing perspectives.

Dr. Clum argued that chiropractic has been ahead of its time for 100 years and "changes in every venue are moving toward what we've been talking about; the population is awakening to the very ideas we have held dear." He described the development of scientific reductionism, noting that now chiropractic's vitalistic emphasis has reached a critical mass of acceptance, as indicated by people's reliance on chiropractic and other forms of alternative care. However, he warned that the profession is in danger of a "premature cognitive commitment" that could inhibit chiropractic from fulfilling its potential. He called on the profession to take confidence in what it has to offer – scientifically sound, low-cost/low-tech

health care, with a message to patients about personal responsibility. "There never has been a better formula for success."

Dr. Winterstein's presentation emphasized the ethical use of philosophy for the sake of patients who deserve a rational, not just emotional, justification for chiropractic care. He took aim at statements from B.J. Palmer that, he asserted, had never been substantiated. He also criticized the use of popular statements about mind-body connectedness to prove chiropractic because they still had to be tested by the methods of science. "I think philosophy is important, but that doesn't mean we have to get into metaphysics, just support our current knowledge and help minister to the sick and suffering."

Dr. Winterstein asserted that philosophical positions that cannot be proved should be abandoned in communications with patients. "We would enjoy far greater progress if we adopted a platform based on science and had the confidence that derives from scientific support. We should move away from the martyrdom complex that currently grips us into a future where we hold our heads up high because the foundation of our knowledge is legitimate."

A philosophy session on Friday featured four influential women in chiropractic, Claudia Anrig, D.C., Pat Gayman, D.C., Meridel Gatterman, D.C., and Agnes Palmer, D.C.

Dr. Anrig declared her intent "to ruffle a few feathers" by advising those who would debunk chiropractic philosophy to start another profession of manual medicine, "and don't let the door hit you on the way out." She urged her listeners "not to be embarrassed to say 'above down inside out'" and to teach that principle to patients.

Dr. Gatterman argued that chiropractic's patient-centered paradigm, rather than being unscientific, is in harmony with science, drawing upon six valid philosophical doctrines of vitalism, wholism, humanism, naturalism, conservatism and rationalism.

Dr. Gayman urged the audience to follow the example of leaders of the profession who demonstrated boldness for the chiropractic cause. She applauded the increase of knowledge in the scientific field but expressed the wish that research go beyond range-of-motion studies. She, too, talked about a growing popular acceptance of some of the tenets of chiropractic and said, "We should reach out to these people to show them that removing the subluxation is the missing link that makes everything work together."

Dr. Agnes Palmer, Dr. David Palmer's widow, discussed her personal spiritual experiences and encouraged the audience not to neglect the spiritual side of their lives. "When you believe and it gets into the heart, it creates hope and can develop into faith."

On Friday afternoon Tom Gelardi, D.C., and James Parker, D.C., added their own perspectives. Dr.

Gelardi, from Sherman College of Straight Chiropractic, argued that chiropractic must safeguard its mission and its emphasis on correcting the subluxation complex. "We can't change chiropractic. We can choose to play the clarinet and call it chiropractic, but it's really fixed. We have to change what we can change. We can change managed care, but we can't change chiropractic. Central to the chiropractic profession is the subluxation. Our profession must focus in order to be sustained."

Gelardi emphasized the importance of innate intelligence yet noted that did not demean the importance of developing educated intelligence or pursuing scientific research as B.J. Palmer had done.

Dr. Parker stressed the need for the chiropractic profession "to expand itself" to understand and "develop a healing consciousness" transmitted to the patient. "D.D. had the new idea. B.J. had the big idea. Now it's time for the whole idea," which he described as the "quality of the quantity flow" of nerve impulses. "We work with the subtle substance of the soul," he said. "We need a passion for chiropractic... and need to commit ourselves to treating the mental, physical and spiritual aspects of our patients."

Later on Friday Marilyn Smith, D.C., and Louis Sportelli, D.C., added their insights.

Dr. Smith recounted her successes in interesting and educating medical doctors about chiropractic. In several instances she has cared for physicians, surgeons and their families with good results, resulting in many referrals. The moral? "We have to work to educate people in what we do. The masses are seeking what we possess. Many other health care providers are seeking what we possess."

Dr. Sportelli called for more commitment to unifying the profession. "We're frequently at odds with each other over things that are irrelevant. We need to debate issues without swearing at each other. We're not that far apart. This is a day of celebration and restoration. We need to celebrate the things that are good."

Sportelli said that a new wellness paradigm awaits chiropractic in the next century, challenging the profession to display the intellectual maturity necessary to step into it.

Others who contributed to the philosophy presentation included Carl S. Cleveland, III, D.C., Galen Price, D.C., and Guy Riekeman, D.C.

Drs. Gerard Clum and James Winterstein provided two views of chiropractic philosophy

# Mock trial teaches doctors

A mock trial, moderated by Rob Sherman, Esq., an attorney from Columbus, Ohio, was one of the liveliest sessions at both Washington and Davenport. The format was a court setting, complete with witnesses and attorneys.

Sherman introduced the sessions by noting that, although many of the observers would never be involved in litigation, the principles would apply to taking of depositions. In fact, knowledge of stringent court requirements and procedures helps keep doctors out of court in the first place.

Dr. Dan Murphy, a California chiropractor, acted as a witness, and Paul Lambert, a Florida attorney, conducted Dr. Murphy's cross-examination.

For the most part, each participant acted out his role seriously, with occasional interruptions and commentary from "Judge" Sherman to show the practical lessons involved. Among them: the need for thorough and accurate documentation, being cautious about assertions under oath, effective use of visual aids, avoiding emotionalism or appeals to philosophy, and showing respect for other health care professionals who might offer opposing testimony.

After the Davenport session, Dr. Catherine Miller, a semi-retired chiropractor from Port Huron, Michigan, said, "Not until about 10 years ago would we have even considered the possibility of going to trial." Yet, she said, the workshop helped her and her chiropractor husband, Dr. Raymond Miller, learn ways to better prepare themselves for the possibility.

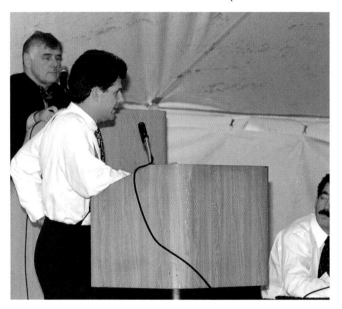

A mock trial proves instructive

Dr. Roy Sweat

# Davenport symposium workshops

Workshops at the Davenport symposium included, as listed in the program by order of presentation:

**Technique:** Activator – Arlan Fuhr, D.C.; Gonstead – Doug Cox, D.C.; Thompson – Wayne Zemelka, D.C.; Flexion Distraction – James Cox, D.C.; SOT – Vern Hagen, D.C.; NUCCA – Albert Berti, D.C.; Atlas Orthogonality – Roy Sweat, D.C.; Diversified – Richard Burns, D.C.; Motion Assisted Adjusting-Leander – Kelli Pearson-Weary, D.C.

**Special Topics:** Spinal Anatomy – Gregory Cramer, D.C.; Spinal Neurophysiology and Somatovisceral Reflexes – Scott Haldeman, D.C., M.D., Ph.D.; Contraindications/Complications – Gregory Plaugher, D.C.; Orthopedic and Neurologic Examinations – Kevin McCarthy, D.C.; Disability Evaluation – Larry Swank, D.C.; Psychosocial Factors – Curtis Rexroth, D.C.; Care During Pregnancy – Joan Fallon, D.C.; General Physical Examination – Gary Tarola, D.C.; Rehabilitation – Kim Christensen, D.C.; Orthotics – Kent Greenawalt and Monte Greenawalt, D.C.; Temporomandibular Joint – Darryl Curl, D.D.S., D.C.

## 15 continuing education credit hours

A total of 15 hours of continuing education credit was available for the Davenport symposium, approved in all states except Ohio and Oklahoma.

# Concurrent tracks in Davenport offer plenty of variety

In addition to the main sessions on history and philosophy, concurrent tracts in Davenport offered education and information to a variety of tastes and interests. Here is a list of those sessions, as they appeared in the program in order of scheduled presentation:

**Thursday**

Diagnostic Imaging in Chiropractic Practice — Russell Erhardt, D.C., Murray Solomon, M.D.; Business Management Part 1 — Larry Markson, D.C.; ACRRT Program/Criteria for Repeat X-Rays — Robert Percuoco, D.C.; Clinical Grand Rounds Part 1 — Moderator: Kevin McCarthy, D.C., panelists: James Cox, D.C., Kelli Pearson-Weary, D.C., Curtis Rexroth, D.C., Thomas Souza, D.C., Larry Swank, D.C.; Chiropractic Assistants Program/Developing Communication Skills — Carla Vincent; Associated Persons Program — Jeanine Graykowski; ACRRT Program/Normal Radiographic Anatomy of the Spine — Dennis Marchiori, D.C.; Chiropractic Assistants Program — Sherry Hodge; Associated Persons Program/Creating the Most Efficient Office Imaginable at Home and in the Workplace — Sandra Phillips; Chiropractic Assistants Program/The CA's Role in Public Relations — Richard Vincent, D.C.; Associated Persons Program — Kaye Rive, B.A., M.A.

**Friday**

Sports Chiropractic — Thomas Souza, D.C., Susan Welsh, D.C.; Technique Grand Rounds — Moderators: Tom Bergmann, D.C., Kevin Bartol, D.C.; panelists: Richard Burns, D.C., Arlan Fuhr, D.C., Jonathan Howat, D.C, Gregory Plaugher, D.C., Marian Schultz, D.C.; ACRRT Program/X-ray Positioning: Boring or Scientific Art? — Garry Krakos, D.C.; Business Management Part 2 — David Kats, D.C.; Chiropractic Assistants and Associated Persons Program — Jacalyn Buettner, D.C.; ACRRT

Dr. Thomas Souza

Program (continued) — Dennis Marchiori, D.C., Garry Krakos, D.C., Robert Percuoco, D.C.; Clinical Grand Rounds Part 2 — Moderator: Kevin McCarthy, D.C., panelists from Part 1; Chiropractic Assistants Program — Paul Peterson, D.C.; Associated Persons Program — Michele Hoffman; Issues in Chiropractic Education and Licensure — Moderator: Meredith Bakke, D.C., panelists: Carl S. Cleveland, III, D.C., Reed Phillips, D.C., Paul Tullio, D.C.; Chiropractic Assistants Program — Martha Dehn; Associated Persons Program/Networking for Personal and Professional Success — Kim Herfert

Dr. Garry Krakos

Dr. Susan Welsh

**Saturday**

Imaging Issues in Chiropractic Practice — Terry Yochum, D.C.; Chiropractors are Primary Physicians not Primary Contact Specialists — Moderator: David A. Chapman-Smith, Esq.; Business Management Grand Rounds — Moderator: Richard Vincent, D.C., panelists: David Kats, D.C., Larry Markson, D.C.; College Presidents' Forum; Chiropractic Assistants Program/Developing Your Role and Purpose as a Great C.A. — Pat Atanas; Associated Persons Program — Sandra Kindred; Imaging for Chiropractors in Their 2nd Century — Moderator: Reed Phillips, D.C., Ph.D.; Panelists: Michael Barry, D.C., Russell Erhardt, D.C., Ian McLean, D.C., Gary Schultz, D.C., Terry Yochum, D.C.; Business Management Part 3 — Richard Vincent, D.C.

# Marker symbolizes chiropractic's roots

The chiropractic profession has made its mark in history, and Chiropractic Centennial Foundation planners were determined to make a literal mark in Davenport, Iowa, where it all began. A similar marker would be placed on the Palmer College campus.

On September 16, 1995, chiropractic and community dignitaries gathered under sunny skies at the downtown corner of Second and Brady streets, the site of the Ryan building where Daniel David Palmer performed the first adjustment on September 18, 1895.

D.D.'s great-granddaughter, Vickie Palmer, chairman of the Palmer Chiropractic University System board of trustees, stood with Pat Gibbs, the mayor of Davenport, and more than 100 Grand Celebration attendees.

"It gives me great pleasure and a feeling of honor to be involved in this chiropractic monument," Ms. Palmer said.

Dr. Fred Barge, immediate past president of the ICA, noted: "The ICA's roots are set in this town of Davenport, Iowa. It's a tremendous occasion for the healing arts in the United States."

Dr. Kurt Hegetschweiler, ACA president, added: "It's an overwhelming feeling to stand here where it all started. We have truly come full circle."

"I kinda think D.D.'s up there smiling down on us today," said CCF president William Holmberg. "This marker truly symbolizes our roots. Remember, take the spirit of the Centennial back home with you."

The large marker, sponsored by the CCF, was made from cast aluminum by an Ohio company. The CCF logo is centered at the top. Arranging for the marker was one of several CCF projects headed up by trustee Glenda Wiese. The marker reads:

*Here at Brady and Second streets, in the former Ryan Building, is the site of the first chiropractic adjustment. On September 18, 1895, Daniel David Palmer, who was practicing as a magnetic healer at the time, repositioned a vertebra in the spine of Harvey Lillard. Palmer reported that, as he intended, the adjustment restored Lillard's hearing. In 1897, Palmer founded the first chiropractic school on this site. In 1905, he moved the school to the present Palmer College of Chiropractic campus "atop Brady Street Hill." By its Centennial year, chiropractic was practiced by an estimated 60,000 chiropractors in 50 countries.*

Glenda Wiese, Dr. Kurt Hegetschweiler, Dr. Fred Barge, Vickie Palmer and Dr. William Holmberg

## "Wouldn't you know it!"

The edge was taken off the exuberance over the Centennial marker when one of the chiropractors attending the ceremony at Second and Brady streets in Davenport noticed a spelling error.

The word *chiropractic* was misspelled in one of its occurrences. It was spelled "chiropratic," without the second "c."

The company doing the casting made the error although the original copy submitted was correct.

"Wouldn't you know it," said the chiropractor who spotted the mistake. "It just shows chiropractic still has a ways to go if people can't even spell the word right."

The marker had to be sent back to the Ohio company that had produced it, to be replaced by another with all the words spelled correctly. Little things mean a lot.

# FIRST CHIROPRACTIC ADJUSTMENT

HERE AT BRADY AND SECOND STREETS, IN THE FORMER RYAN BUILDING, IS THE SITE OF THE FIRST CHIROPRACTIC ADJUSTMENT. ON SEPTEMBER 18, 1895, DANIEL DAVID PALMER, WHO WAS PRACTICING AS A MAGNETIC HEALER AT THE TIME, REPOSITIONED A VERTEBRA IN THE SPINE OF HARVEY LILLARD. PALMER REPORTED THAT, AS HE HAD INTENDED, THE ADJUSTMENT RESTORED LILLARD'S HEARING. IN 1897 PALMER FOUNDED THE FIRST CHIROPRACTIC SCHOOL ON THIS SITE. IN 1905 HE MOVED THE SCHOOL TO THE PRESENT PALMER COLLEGE OF CHIROPRACTIC CAMPUS "ATOP BRADY STREET HILL." BY ITS CENTENNIAL YEAR, 1995, CHIROPRATIC WAS PRACTICED BY AN ESTIMATED 60,000 CHIROPRACTORS IN 50 COUNTRIES.

ERECTED BY THE
CHIROPRACTIC CENTENNIAL FOUNDATION

# Centennial program arranged for students

Chiropractic colleges helped their students celebrate the Centennial, in some cases subsidizing their attendance. For the Davenport celebration, Palmer College made arrangements for not only its students but students from other colleges who couldn't pay for Centennial tickets.

They were invited to the "Evening with Ray Charles" at The Mark of the Quad-Cities. There was an educational program at the former Masonic Temple, now called Lyceum Hall. It included some of the speakers appearing a few blocks away at the Davenport RiverCenter. On Friday morning they could hear x-ray expert Dr. Russell Erhardt and Dr. James Cox, father of the Cox Lumbar Distraction Technique. On Friday afternoon Dr. Susan Welsh discussed sports chiropractic, and the chiropractic documentary was shown. On Saturday the speakers were Dr. Douglas Cox, demonstrating the full-spine technique, and Dr. David Kats, discussing how to set up a chiropractic practice.

Free food is always a big hit with students, and in conjunction with the Centennial students got two continental breakfasts, a lunch and admission to the Palmer Centennial barbecue.

This Japanese contingent reminded chiropractors that their profession is international

# Centennial celebration is international affair

The entire Centennial and the Davenport gala in particular were international in scope not only because of continuing education that revealed the progress and contribution of chiropractors outside the U.S. but in the very presence of people reportedly from more than 29 foreign countries. Attendees outside workshops at the Davenport RiverCenter, Adler Theatre and Blackhawk Hotel could be heard discussing chiropractic in many languages seldom heard in Davenport.

Sira Borges, M.D., D.C., one of six chiropractors in Brazil: "Coming to the Centennial Celebration was a wonderful way to meet with colleagues. When you're practicing in another country, you're often isolated from your peers because there are so few of you. Even so, I find practicing in Brazil very rewarding. Patients love chiropractic because it gets such good results. They come from other states that are often many hours away to see me."

The presence of chiropractors from Africa, Australia, Canada, Europe, Hong Kong, Iran, Japan, Mexico and New Zealand was living proof chiropractic is growing worldwide.

"Through the efforts of organizations like the World Federation of Chiropractic (WFC), representatives from chiropractic colleges as well as individual practitioners, chiropractic is rapidly gaining worldwide acceptance," said CCF trustee and WFC secretary-general David A. Chapman-Smith, Esq. "In the last few years we have sent delegations to Brazil, Mexico, China, Thailand, and (before the Davenport celebration) a WFC and Palmer College of Chiropractic delegation represented chiropractic at the annual meeting of the World Health Organization in Switzerland. These efforts are resulting in significant progress in establishing new chiropractic colleges and formal licensure for chiropractic in many countries outside North America. Chiropractic is especially attractive for patients in developing countries because of its treatment efficacy and cost-effectiveness."

# Thousands mob Palmer barbecue

The barbecue hosted by Palmer College on the Palmer campus was one of the best attended of all Centennial sessions. Included were a philosophy session and other speeches, a dance and generous helpings of food.

At least 5,000 people were served chicken or porkchop sandwiches, sweet corn, baked beans, potato chips, apple cobbler and beverages, including 39 kegs of beer. The Davenport police department estimated the crowd coming and going throughout the evening at 10,000.

Other colleges held receptions in Davenport, among them Sherman College of Straight Chiropractic, Life College and Life Chiropractic College-West, Logan College of Chiropractic, Los Angeles College of Chiropractic, National College of Chiropractic, New York Chiropractic College, Northwestern College of Chiropractic and Western States Chiropractic College.

**The Palmer barbecue - conversation and plenty of food**

# Historical papers win awards

Four historical research awards, each worth $2,500, were given to applicants who had the further honor of presenting their original papers at the historical symposium. According to Stefan Pallister, D.C., educational program director, the judges reviewed each proposed project for thoroughness and completeness, the clarity of the proposal and the originality of the work. "The judges considered the scope of the topic, as well as the impact the subject of the study had on the profession, in making their decisions."

Winning papers were:
• "The Evolution of Chiropractic Technique and Analysis" – Robert Cooperstein, M.A., D.C., Palmer College of Chiropractic West, San Jose, California.
• "The Man Who Hated Chiropractors: Morris Fishbein of the AMA" – Joseph H. Donahue, D.C., Peru, Illinois.
• "The Survival of Chiropractic: Evaluating the Denial Syndrome of Historical Medicine, 1950-94" – Russell W. Gibbons, Pittsburgh, Pennsylvania.

• "J.J. – The Story of Joseph Janse: A Chiropractor" – Reed B. Phillips, D.C., and Joey Janse, D.C., Los Angeles College of Chiropractic, Whittier, California.

Additional prizes were awarded in Davenport for history papers. They included:
• "William C. Schultze, M.D., D.C. (1890-1936)" – Joseph Keating, Jr., Ph.D., Whittier, California, and William Rehm, D.C., first prize of $2,500.
• "The Making of a European Chiropractor in the 1920's: Fred Illi and the Universal Chiropractic College" – Pierre-Louis Gaucher-Peslherbe, D.C., Ph.D., France, second prize of $1,500.
• "Did Osteopathy 'Borrow' the Chiropractic Short Lever Adjustment (the Core of All Modern Manipulative Techniques) Without Giving Palmer Credit?" – James W. Brantingham, D.C., Thousand Oaks, California, third prize of $1,000.

121

# Everything is "wonderful" in chiropractic's hometown

*"Being here has given me more excitement about being a chiropractor."*

Davenport was a different ball game from Washington. That the birthplace of chiropractic is a smaller town had much to do with it, as did the fact The Fountainhead is there. The chiropractors were making a pilgrimage to Mecca, many for the first time. "I've always wanted to see where it all began," said one bright-eyed and beautiful visitor outside the Palmer mansion, and she was typical of many.

The Palmer College Campus Guides estimated 4,000 people toured the mansion, staring curiously at the rustic furnishings from the Arts and Crafts era, and at B.J. and Mabel's collection of memorabilia, chess sets, figurines and other artifacts from their world travels. Some of the visitors brought their children along and patiently explained the exotic things they saw. A couple of times the line to get in was literally a block long.

Externs and faculty doctors at the Palmer Chiropractic Clinics performed 3,000 adjustments, three times the normal amount for the period, despite the fact the Clinics were on a shortened schedule.

A big crowd toured the Palmer Mansion

When the chiropractors and their spouses or significant others walked around downtown Davenport to get a sandwich or a drink, they were warmly greeted by restaurant employees and others. Davenport, unlike Washington where conventions are a dime a dozen, appreciated the chiropractors being there and said so. Television crews and newspaper reporters showed up at the RiverCenter frequently, and the message came through loud and clear that, yes, this is a big deal.

Inside the RiverCenter everybody was caught up in the excitement. In some instances, presenters at the philosophy sessions could get a standing ovation practically for showing up. The word "wonderful" was uttered thousands of times in a few days and directed at everything from the program, to the

These banners told Davenport it was time to celebrate chiropractic

exhibitors, to the Davenport weather, to the Mississippi River, to the entertainment, to the Palmer Mansion, to the placing of the historical marker, to the fireworks on the levee.

"Being here has given me more excitement about being a chiropractor, and I'll be able to bring that enthusiasm back to the students I teach at Anglo-European College of Chiropractic in Bournemouth," said Ida Norgaard, D.C., of Bournemouth, England. "Here the big lecturers fire you up. You don't see that so much in England."

The exhibitors, some of whom had threatened to sue the CCF after they were stood up in Washington, were busy with traffic during most of the Davenport gala. The CCF had shrewdly laid out things so that people wanting to register or get a snack in the RiverCenter had to go through the exhibit hall. In Washington the exhibitors had been on another level, and it was possible to attend all the Centennial education and entertainment without ever walking through the displays.

The street was blocked off between the two sections of the RiverCenter, and parked in the middle was a yellow Cadillac. It had been B.J.'s car, brought to the Centennial by Dr. Sid Williams, president of Life Chiropractic College, and it provided a photo op for hundreds of chiropractors and chiropractic students. During many hours of the Centennial program that section of the street was packed with laughing, crying and hugging people.

Davenport was a love feast.

**Chiropractors practically took over downtown Davenport**

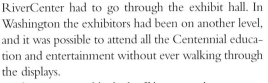

**B.J.'s car provided photo opportunities**

**Kisses for Dr. Russell Erhardt from Drs. Jerilynn Kaibel and Marilyn Smith**

123

The Chiropractic
message was
everywhere

Hugs aplenty

Future doctors?

124

"D.D.'s Place' - the
Palmer College
Admissions booth

Crowds paid
rapt attention

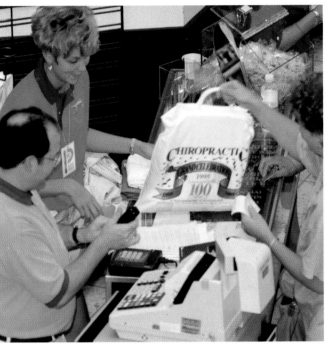

Centennial stuff was grabbed up

U.S. Senator
Tom Harkin
(D-Iowa)

Brotherhood

A banner
celebration

A Scottish air

125

# Whatever you want, vendors have it

Step right up. Interested in a therapeutic hydro massage unit? How about a desk calendar? Or maybe you'd like to refinance. Just about any product or service you could desire related to chiropractic care was on display in the Centennial exhibit halls. To name a few – x-ray film processors, air filters, association displays, physical therapy systems, TMJ splints, financing chiropractic equipment, patient education materials, radiation shields, nutritional supplements, adjusting tables, heating pads, management software, posture corrective devices, patient documentation systems, cervical/lumbar supports, advertising services, equipment leasing, college admissions, computerized injury assessment, radiographic systems, herbal teas, diagnostic ultrasound scanners, educational posters. ...

**Vendors boosted product exposure in Davenport's RiverCenter**

**Dozens of exhibits of things chiropractic**

# Golf tournaments promote fellowship

The golf outings before the Washington and Davenport galas provided scores of chiropractors and their spouses relaxed fun and fellowship not to mention some nice prizes for the winning golfers.

Drs. William Erbe and Larry Sigulinsky organized the tournaments at Washington and Davenport respectively. More than 100 participated at the Andrews Air Force Base course near Washington and 144 at Glynns Creek north of Davenport. The doctors reported that both courses were in excellent condition, and the weather was "perfect." Deer romping across a fairway in Davenport provided an extra touch.

Dr. Erbe said the tournament was organized with a measure of flexibility so that people could play along with old friends. "The emphasis was on having a great time rather than worrying too much about the competitive aspect of things." Fifty-two prizes – mostly plaques and gift certificates at the pro shop – were given out. "It was an ideal getaway from the serious issues we were discussing at the convention."

Dr. Sigulinsky likewise reported that the Davenport tournament was well received. Winners got golf balls, bags and clubs as well as plaques. "We had a shotgun start, so everybody finished in good time." Dr. Sigulinsky said that a notable aspect of the Davenport tourney was the participation by gala attendees from several foreign countries. "We matched people from different parts of the world as well as different parts of the country. It was one more way we worked to broaden our understanding and deepen our respect for one another in the profession."

Fellowship on the golf course...

Drs. Lou Latimer, William Holmberg and William Erbe helped organize the Washington event

# "Defining moments" captured on canvas

Trustee Glenda Wiese steered the commissioning of 12 original works of art, capturing defining moments in chiropractic history. The project stemmed from a proposal to the AHC by Russell Gibbons, editor of *Chiropractic History*, and Dr. Louis Sportelli of Palmerton, Pennsylvania, a long-time AHC member.

"A Centennial commemoration in art should celebrate the significant events of chiropractic's history," their proposal said. "The concepts for art commissions should capture in painting the history and diversity of chiropractic."

The 12 original oil and acrylic paintings were produced by five artists. An AHC committee helped research historical highlights and considered prospective sketches from artists in California, Florida, New York, Missouri and Iowa. Final selection of 12 paintings by five artists was made by a joint committee of the CCF and the AHC.

Bids for the paintings were accepted by silent auction, with live auctions at the Davenport gala. Bidding for each piece of art started at $2,000.

## The 12 paintings:

*The First Adjustment*, by John Dyeuss, recreates Daniel David Palmer's history-making adjustment of Harvey Lillard in the Ryan Block in downtown Davenport, Iowa, in 1895.

The fire of *B.J. Palmer Lecturing at a PSC Lyceum* was captured in the Ted McElhiney painting, set in 1921. The annual Lyceum, later Homecoming, provided education and motivation for practicing chiropractors, who often put forth great effort to attend year after year.

*Mabel Palmer in the Classroom*, by Robert Lawson, salutes the contribution made by the "First Lady of Chiropractic." Mabel Palmer's historic role included helping financially stabilize the Palmer School and leading the way for women in the profession.

In *Patients and Chiropractors Marching for Chiropractic*, artist Jack Smith represented the fight for licensure. Public pressure and patient action committees eventually produced chiropractic laws in all 50 states. Smith chose a scene from Ohio in the 1920s for this picture.

*The First Adjustment*, by John Dyeuss

*B.J. Palmer Lecturing at a PSC Lyceum*, by Ted McElhiney

*Mabel Palmer in the Classroom*, by Robert Lawson

*Patients and Chiropractors Marching for Chiropractic*, by Jack Smith

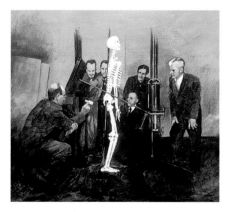
*Willard Carver Fighting for Legislation in Oklahoma*, by Robert Lawson

*Fred Illi Representing Chiropractic Around the World*, by Jack Smith

*Willard Carver Fighting for Legislation in Oklahoma*, by Robert Lawson, shows an animated Carver imploring the legislature in 1917.

*Fred Illi Representing Chiropractic Around the World*, by Jack Smith, portrays the spread of chiropractic to Europe and elsewhere overseas. Original research by Illi in Switzerland, Gillet in Belgium and others contributed to the success. The artist represents Illi demonstrating at a European Chiropractic Congress clinical session.

*The First Full-Spine X-ray*, by Robert Lawson, highlights the importance of radiology to the growth, credibility and effectiveness of the chiropractic profession.

*Howard, Leo and Dan Spears*, by Robert Lawson, shows them in front of Spears Hospital, the largest chiropractic hospital in history, which lasted 40 years in Denver.

*Chiropractic Educational Accreditation*, by Jack Smith, represents that major step in the legitimizing of the profession. During the reform period countless negotiations were held with the U.S. Office of Education prior to Council on Chiropractic Education recognition. Shown are Joseph Janse, Jack Wolfe, Orville Hiddie and Leonard Fay.

*Earl Homewood and Joe Janse Representing Educational Reform*, by Robert Lawson, pictures the 40-year struggle for reorganization of chiropractic educational standards. Homewood and Janse are shown at the National College of Chiropractic.

*Going to Jail for Chiropractic*, by Robert Lawson, shows a chiropractor imprisoned behind bars with a policeman standing guard. Following the trial, conviction and imprisonment of D.D. Palmer in 1906, hundreds, perhaps thousands, of chiropractors went to jail through as late as 1974.

*The Wilk, et. al, Court Victory*, by Kirk Miller, captures the legal victory that ended the American Medical Association's boycott of chiropractic. Subsequently several medical organizations published statements that medical doctors were free to associate professionally with doctors of chiropractic.

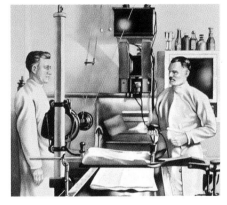
*The First Full-Spine X-ray*, by Robert Lawson

*Howard, Leo and Dan Spears*, by Robert Lawson

*Chiropractic Educational Accreditation*, by Jack Smith

*Earl Homewood and Joe Janse Representing Educational Reform*, by Robert Lawson

*Going to Jail for Chiropractic*, by Robert Lawson

*The Wilk, et. al, Court Victory*, by Kirk Miller

Salute

An Evening with Ray Charles:
A Salute to the Palmer Family
was the entertainment highlight
of the Centennial
Photograph by Wanda Simmons

*to the Palmers*

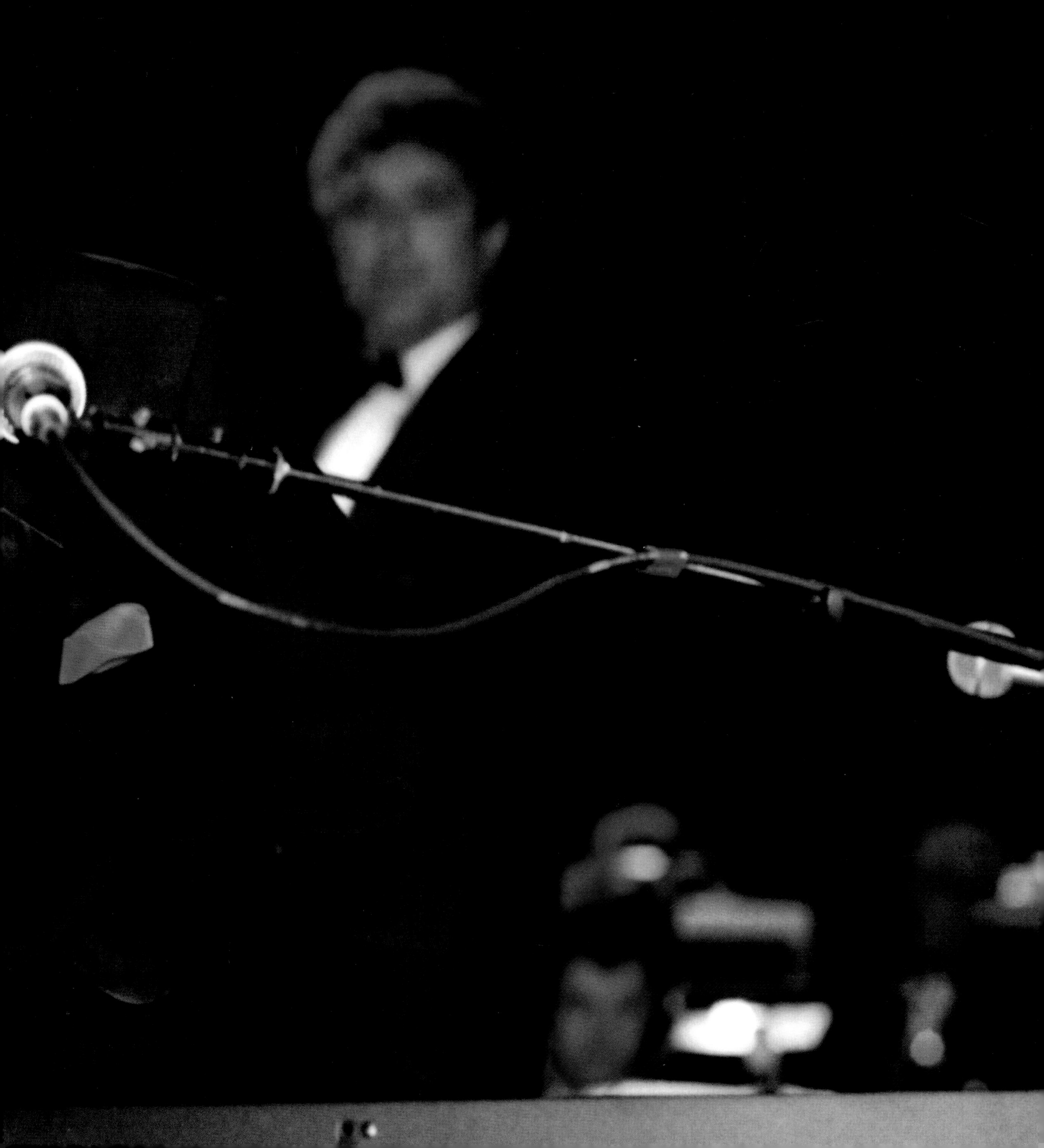

# "Evening with Ray Charles" honors Palmers, highlights Davenport gala

The classiest and best attended entertainment program of the Centennial was not a CCF project but one put on by Palmer College of Chiropractic. An estimated 11,000 people, including many community leaders and other guests, filled the Mark of the Quad-Cities, the thriving new concert center in Moline across the river from Davenport, for "An Evening with Ray Charles: A Salute to the Palmer Family."

The program, which was coordinated by Juan Nodarse, opened with two stirring numbers by the red-coated Moline Boys Choir, each with an accompanying video presentation on a huge screen and on oversized television monitors. The first video, presented to the theme from *The Lion King*, "Circle of Life," featured scenes of animals and humans from babies to the elderly. It ended with a dramatic visual effect, the sparkling planet earth settling into giant cupped hands. After the actor playing D.D. Palmer came on stage with some opening remarks, the Choir went into an upbeat rendering of "Consider Yourself" from *Oliver*. The accompanying video showed footage from throughout the Centennial year – a musical and visual call for unity and fellowship.

Next D.D. introduced Michael Crawford, Chancellor of the Palmer Chiropractic University System, who brought on President Virgil Strang, D.C., of Palmer College and Michael Chimes, D.C., president of the PCC International Alumni Association. Drs. Strang and Chimes presented a narrative reading about D.D., B.J., Mabel, David and the Palmer daughters while video images of each appeared overhead. Crawford next brought on Dr. William Holmberg, Dr. Roger Hulsebus and Dr. Marilyn Smith, the latter two of whom are Palmer trustees as well as trustees of the CCF.

Vickie Palmer came on stage to accept a plaque, which read in part: "In honor of D.D. Palmer, who discovered a new path to good health, understood its profound implications, translated them into an effective form of natural health care and inspired the promulgation of the philosophy, art and science called chiropractic." Dr. Strang then stepped forward, noting that history is uncertain as to whether D.D. Palmer ever gave himself a degree. To remedy that Strang declared a convocation and bestowed posthumously on D.D. Palmer the degree of Doctor of Chiropractic from Palmer College.

Vickie Palmer, D.D.'s great-granddaughter, made a few remarks, calling on today's chiropractors to bear the brunt of daunting challenges as did the

Juan Nodarse

*"In honor of D.D. Palmer, who discovered a new path to good health. ..."*

**The Moline Boys Choir entertained the crowd accompanied by music videos**

chiropractic pioneers who had gone before. The actor D.D. introduced an original musical composition "You've Been There for Me," which was sung by Jenny Frogley, wife of Dr. Scott Frogley and the daughter-in-law of well-known Davenport chiropractor Ronald Frogley. A third video with footage and photographs from the Palmer College archives was shown as she sang the tribute. She finished with an upbeat version of the Palmer song featured at Homecoming the last few years, "Palmer Proud."

The chiropractic part of the show had the audience pumped up for Ray Charles, who came on to a thunderous ovation. Charles was accompanied by a large symphony orchestra, which added another touch of class to the formal event. His performance was vintage, with a full set of his many popular, country, and rhythm and blues hits. At the climax of the performance, his rendition of "America the Beautiful" brought tears to many eyes... and a standing ovation.

Drs. Virgil Strang and Michael Chimes

Vickie Palmer accepts a plaque honoring her great-grandfather

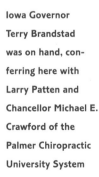

Iowa Governor Terry Brandstad was on hand, conferring here with Larry Patten and Chancellor Michael E. Crawford of the Palmer Chiropractic University System

The salute to the Palmers included a dramatic reading about the Palmers by Drs. Virgil Strang and Michael Chimes, a plaque honoring D.D. Palmer presented to Vickie Palmer and an honorary degree bestowed on D.D. Palmer

Jenny Frogley sings
an original musical
composition written
for the Palmer family

The Legendary
Genius of Soul

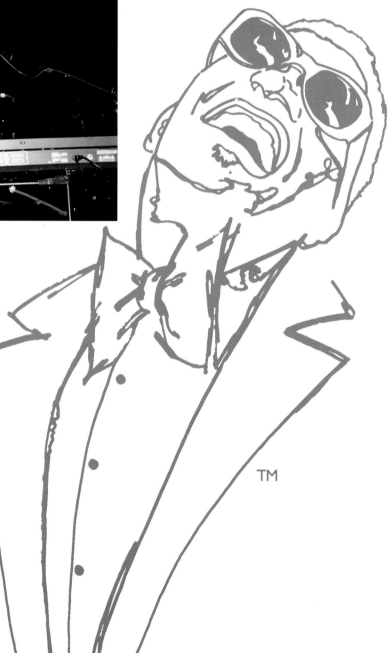

TM

Drs. Agnes Palmer,
Maxine McMullen.
Lorene Price and
Galen Price

From left, Jenny Palmer Sutton, Sara Sutton, Kermit Sutton, Matthew
Sutton, Agnes M.H. Palmer, D.C., Bonnie Palmer McCloskey, Donald E.
Pruter and Vickie A. Palmer

Dr. and Mrs. Trevor Ireland
and Dr. and Mrs. Don Betz

Dr. Marilyn Smith, Dr. Michael
Chimes, Dr. Roger Hulsebus and
Michael Crawford

135

# Centennial's grand finale is warm and happy affair

The Grand Finale of the Centennial was a picnic in the park on the Davenport levee not far from where the first chiropractic adjustment was performed on Harvey Lillard. It was a relaxed and happy affair, with an auction for the Centennial paintings, good food and drink, lots of fellowship and warmly received entertainment.

The Ray Charles concert was Thursday, and it was the Davenport gala's entertainment showpiece. Because of budget cuts, the CCF had to eliminate other marquee entertainment from the picnic Saturday, but nobody seemed to mind. They gave hearty applause to Alan Thicke, who gave an outstanding performance in the band shell similar to the one in Washington. Other entertainers were David Kell, D.C., a talented juggler; Jim Warner, D.C., dressed as B.J. Palmer; Trish Kelly-Knight, who performed musical numbers, and Acappella, the quartet who had also performed in Washington. The actor David Richards as D.D. Palmer was again the emcee.

Although the food was tasty, feeding the thousands who came to the Davenport levee for the grand finale turned into a problem. Apparently hundreds of people failed to get served.

A postmortem indicated that, although evidently enough food was ordered, confusion over serving meant some people took all they could eat while others did without. There were several tents each featuring different cuisines, but the idea was that each person was supposed to get their meal at one tent. Signage was unclear, some of the tents ran out of food, and many people visited several tents before late-comers had a chance. After the Centennial, more than a hundred people called the CCF office to complain. Some were only mildly put out, but others wanted their money refunded. A total of 65 people got partial refunds.

Despite all that, most of those in LeClaire Park seemed in a mellow mood. They were being entertained on a nice evening along the Mississippi River. Although there had been a threat of rain, it never happened. Many were a bit nostalgic. They would never see another Centennial, and they were feeling very good about their overall Centennial experience. Old friendships had been renewed and new ones made. A spirit of common commitment and comraderie transcended any disappointments. When a fireworks display finished off the evening, the chiropractic family clapped and cheered and hugged.

Their Centennial was over.

**D.D. and the doctor with the hat were on hand in Davenport**

The picnic
at LeClaire
Park

B.J. and
D.D. live
again

Auctioning
the original
paintings

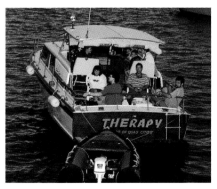

Watching the
show from the
Mississippi River

137

**The CCF planners were applauded on stage**

Trish Kelly-Knight

Alan Thicke

Acappella

**Some of the beautiful people**

Finishing up
with a bang

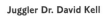

Juggler Dr. David Kell

The picnic in
Davenport
drew people
from around
the world

Vickie Palmer
and her husband,
Donald E. Pruter

# Looking Back on the Grand Celebration

*When it was all over, the Centennial had provided an abundance of education, brought professional issues and strengths into clearer focus, offered great opportunities for fellowship, broken even financially, and produced a bonding within the profession like nothing in the previous 100 years. It was no panacea, but it strengthened the profession to move ahead.*

## Centennial "reminds us how big it all can be"

How can the Chiropractic Centennial be evaluated? Who is in the best position to do so? The CCF planners have their memories and opinions as do thousands who attended the events. The reaction of many more thousands in the profession who did not attend is impossible to gauge. One thing is clear: The CCF accomplished most of its projects and goals.

*"A spirit of cooperation will last in the memories of those who were there."*

One was to celebrate the profession's growth of 100 years, saluting the struggles and successes of those who had gone before. The kickoff luncheon and evening program had a special "electricity," to use Dr. Kerwin Winkler's phrase, and the gala history sessions, the documentary, the audio tapes and oral histories, and the book, *Chiropractic: An Illustrated History*, all contributed toward meeting that goal with flying colors. The Centennial deepened the profession's sense of its own colorful history and culture, heightening awareness of what chiropractors hold in common.

For Dr. Guy Riekeman and others, celebrating the accomplishments of the chiropractic pioneers was quite personal. Several times Dr. Riekeman talked about his father, who served more than 40 years in the profession. "When he died, there was not a satisfactory way to mark the moment, to thank him for all he had done for others." For Dr. Carl S. Cleveland, III, the salute to the pioneers was really poignant, for his father passed away during the Centennial year. Drs. Russell Erhardt, John Grostic, Robert Hulsebus and J. Clay Thompson, considered ground-breakers, mentors and leaders by so many, also died in that time period. How fine they could see their profession come together for a Grand Celebration!

**Determined to keep the profession strong...**

**Many hands helped produce the Centennial celebration**

Another CCF goal was to recognize scientific advancement and promote more research. The scientific symposium, with appearances by prominent health care scientists, as well as the dozens of workshops, research awards, publication of proceedings – they all underscored the importance of science to the profession's future. As several observed, it would be a mistake to conclude that the low attendance at Washington represented lack of interest in science by the mass of the profession. After all, many could only attend a single gala. Finances, family vacation plans, a desire to make a pilgrimage to chiropractic's birthplace, any number of factors could have influenced the choice to come to Davenport.

For those who went to Washington, the presentations of the profession's leading lights, as well as of non-chiropractors praising the virtues and potential of chiropractic, was a boost to their confidence. "The magnitude of the Celebration is awesome," said Dr. Mark Deitch and his fiancee, Dr. Mimi Taitz, who drove 10 hours from Atlanta to

Washington to be a part of history. "It's great to see all the chiropractors come together and see the greatest in the profession."

David A. Chapman-Smith, Esq. said: "There's a difference between a pumped up, false pride and the real pride that recognizes our good people and their accomplishments. When we heard Dr. Gordon Waddell, a leading figure in European medicine, say that chiropractic, not medicine, has the correct health model – that tells us how far recognition of this profession has come. We deserve to be proud of what we have done and are doing."

What was learned about that looming bugaboo managed care? Plenty. Chiropractors were told in no uncertain terms they need to adapt. They could no longer "sit outside and throw stones at the system." They also learned all the other health care professions face at least equal challenges in changing their ways. One of the surprising themes to emerge from the Washington plenary sessions was there are real possibilities for chiropractors as gate-

**Dr. Scott Haldeman helped tell the world that chiropractic has a scientific foundation**

**Dr. Jerilynn Kaibel and Donald M. Petersen, Jr.**

keepers in managed care situations. The Centennial helped clarify many issues. The educational sessions were precisely that – educational.

Dr. Virgil Strang, president of Palmer College, observed: "You know, I was standing in class the other day and suddenly it hit me what managed care is really all about. Think about that expression *managed health care*. It reflects the fact people need help managing their health. The management of money by insurance companies is not managing health. So it will not be sufficient to reform the health care system. Who in the whole world is better equipped to manage health than chiropractors, who recognize that health management begins before people get sick? We face a terrific opportunity!"

Another goal was to raise public consciousness about chiropractic. The Rose Parade float and the successful public relations efforts contributed to meeting that goal, although public consciousness is hard to measure even with surveys, and so far none has been taken in this case. The public relations campaign came at a fortuitous time, to say the least. The release of the AHCPR guideline and the public's

embrace of alternative care added credibility to chiropractic's claim as an alternative to invasive procedures.

Especially the documentary, arriving as the public takes a fresh look at the health care system and its alternatives, is likely to have a powerful impact on those who see it. Its message has already made an impression, judging by the many chiropractors reporting favorable reactions from patients and community acquaintances.

It became evident from the Centennial that there is probably more public support for chiropractic than even chiropractors imagined. As noted by Dr. Gerard Clum, president of Life West, public acceptance of chiropractic has reached a critical mass. The chiro-bashing of *"20/20"* and *Consumer Reports* would have done more damage a few years ago, but now the public takes it in stride. The question now is, how do I pick a *good* chiropractor, not, should I *go* to a chiropractor.

The goal of encouraging profession-wide participation fell short of expectations. The kickoff generated tremendous energy to motivate the chiroprac-

Exhibitors showed confidence in the profession

The Rose Parade float will remain a bright memory

Dr. William Holmberg, D.D. Palmer, Mary Rowe

143

back home. Yet there's many a slip twixt the cup and the lip. Despite all the mailings, newsletters, chiropractic media features, etc., only about 10 percent of the profession participated in the two gala celebrations. Dr. Lou Latimer took it personally: "I'm saddened that our profession did not support the grandest celebration it may ever have opportunity to witness."

Of course, gala numbers don't tell the whole story. Thousands of chiropractors and chiropractic students observed the Centennial in conjunction with college or state association celebrations. The actor playing D.D. Palmer made appearances at several of those events, philosophy lectures were held and so forth. Who knows how many chiropractors went to neither Washington nor Davenport but were nonetheless glued to their televisions for the Rose Parade, or even brought patients into their offices to view the documentary? How many will respond to raised public consciousness about chiropractic with more vigorous patient education programs? How many will hold their heads up higher?

Those who came were impressed with the profession's scientific progress and the global nature of today's chiropractic. The result couldn't help but be a less parochial outlook. "It's so impressive to see the thousands of chiropractors from all over the world," commented Dr. Enrique Benet Canut of Mexico City and president of the Latin American

Federation of Chiropractic. And it was impressive he and so many others came from far away.

How about that most ambitious goal, helping unify the profession by Centennial involvement? Well, anybody who read the chiropractic media during and after the Centennial year knows the Grand Celebration was no panacea. A spectrum of issues is still under heated debate, although it does seem that certain fringe groups like Orthopractic have lost steam. Did the show of strength and unity during the Centennial contribute to putting them on the run? Possibly.

Certainly Centennial activities frequently bridged philosophical differences. Younger chiropractors and students listened with respect to the "old lions" of the profession. One young doctor with a scientific bent was watching one of the "spizzerinctum" sessions when a similarly oriented colleague sidled up and whispered, "Doesn't this stuff turn your stomach?" To which the first replied: "Actually, I kind of like it. More of us could use that commitment."

Still, the profession's philosophical gap is deep intellectually and emotionally. That was painfully evident at times, as when one presenter told those of the more medical inclination to "not let the door hit you on the way out." Such incidents, though, were few. Far more common was the attitude expressed by Dr. Louis Sportelli, who remarked about people of differing philosophies being in the same room

**Health care experts had much to share**

**Mr. and Mrs Kent Greenawalt and Dr. and Mrs. Monte Greenawalt**

without swearing at each other. "This is a day of celebration and restoration. We need to celebrate the things that are good."

That's what thousands did. They put aside worries about managed care and professional politics and concentrated on how much becoming Doctors of Chiropractic had meant to the quality of their lives and those of their patients. By Davenport they were ready to have fun. People who hadn't seen each other for many years rekindled friendships. It was a time to relive memories, to establish professional continuity, to rejoice in the company of similarly dedicated professionals. Celebration time – come on!

Dr. Jerilynn Kaibel put it this way: "As doctors of chiropractic we are too often driven by crisis – celebrating was a new aspect to our psyche. With a few exceptions, I believe everyone attempted to work together for a common goal."

That a bonding took place as never before is simply undeniable. The chauvinism of which college they attended, what view of this or that procedure they held, what place in the profession's political matrix they aspired to – all of that was diminished in the warm fellowship and commitment to a common cause, at least for a time. As Glenda Wiese observed: "A spirit of cooperation will last in the memories of those who were there."

In short, the Centennial was the furthest thing from a wake. It most assuredly was closer to a coming out party.

It strengthened a spirit characteristic of the profession since D.D. and B.J. Palmer and the rest of the pioneers. A common thread ran through the hard work of preparation, through the many enthusiastic presentations on history, technique, philosophy and science, and through the thousands of handshakes, shutter clicks, hugs and kisses. The common thread was pride, that clenched fist of determination to press on.

Dr. Michael Hulsebus put it simply: "Chiropractic has survived all of its obstacles for 100 years. It will remain part of the health care delivery system now and forever."

Dr. Riekeman put it eloquently: "Sometimes in the midst of survival we forget how big the possibilities of our life can and should be. Thank you, B.J., Dad, the profession that arrived in Davenport, those who gave to put chiropractic on TV. ... You reminded me, again, how big it all can be."

And you know how Dr. Holmberg put it: "The Centennial was fantastic!"

Highlighting history

In touch with the action

Sharing cake and a good laugh

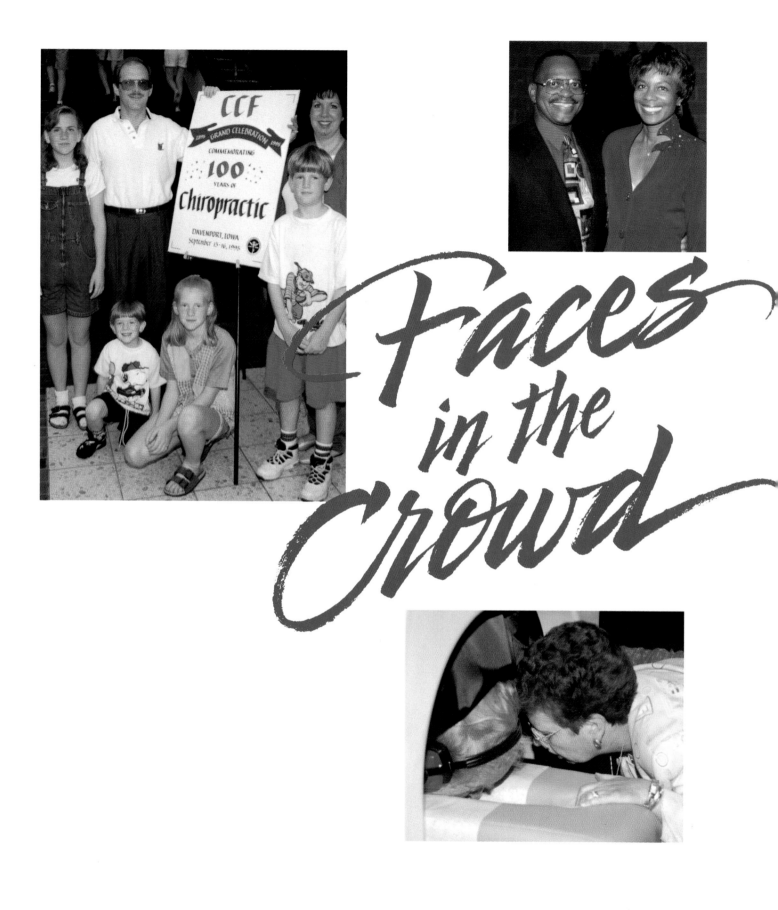

Faces
in the
Crowd

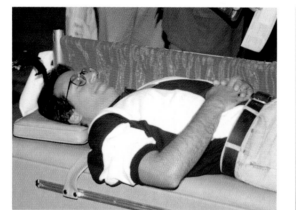

# The CCF thanks these people who made the Celebration Grand!

## Sapphire Sponsor $1,000 (Cont.)

Dr. Nancy Elliott
Dr. Neil Elliott
Dr. Russell Erhardt
Dr. Norris A. Erickson
Dr. Charles M. Evans
Dr. James P. Fallon
Dr. Jeffrey S. Fedorko
Mr. Richard Flaherty
Focus Practice Management
Mrs. Pat M. Fraley-Morrow
Dr. Andre Gaulard
Dr. Salvatore Gennero
Dr. Nelson T. Goff
Dr. Robert J. Goodman
Dr. Billy D. Grant
Greater Boston Chiropractic Society
Dr. Kim Green-Deslauriers
Mr. Kent Greenawalt
Dr. John P. Grumish
Dr. Ray T. Hanson
Dr. Christopher L. Harrison
Dr. Bradley Hennen
Dr. Mariode T. Hermida
Dr. Don Herndon
Dr. Elmer Hester
Dr. John & Wende A. Hofmann
Dr. William F. Holmberg
Dr. Peter A. Holst
Dr. Volkhard V. Homann
Dr. Marie Hopping
Dr. P. Reginald Hug
Dr. Michael Hulsebus
Dr. James Hulsebus
Dr. Robert Hulsebus
Dr. Roger D. Hulsebus
Dr. Dallas D. Humble
Dr. William F. Hynan
Dr. Richard Irby
Dr. Virginia S. Irby
Dr. Gary Jacob
Dr. Marcus G. Jones
Japanese Chiropractic Association
Dr. Shawn R. Jones
Dr. Palmera Kabana
Dr. Charles J. Keller
Dr. Marcia S. Kesten
Dr. Marvin F. Klaes
Dr. Thomas Klesmit
Dr. Gary P. Kliebenstein
Dr. Kenneth J. Koehler
Dr. Eugene Kolenda
Dr. Charles A. Krieger

Dr. Edward L. Kropf, Jr.
Dr. Suzan I. Kudick
Dr. Kathleen M. Lamack
Dr. George E. Langdon
Dr. Louis P. Latimer
Dr. Alan J. Lichter
Dr. Eugene C. Lof
Dr. James M. Loftus
Dr. Edward M. Long
Dr. Patricia Lorence
Dr. Kevin Lowey
Dr. Scott B. Macaulay
Dr. A. Martin
Dr. E.G. Marty
Dr. Lee Masterson
Dr. Theresa McAuliffe
Dr. J.R. McCanse
Dr. E.J. McGinnis
Dr. Rick McMichael
Dr. Steven J. McNeal
Miami Valley Chiropractic Society, 8th District of OSCA
Dr. Daniel A. Michalec
Dr. Dennis W. Miller
Montana Chiropractic Physiotherapy Council
Dr. Richard C. Mooneyham
Dr. J. Ray Morgan
Dr. Arthur G. Mork
Dr. Esther A. Mork
Dr. Wesley S. Mullen, Jr.
Dr. Ken Murkowski
National Upper Cervical Chiropractic Association
Dr. Mark Newcomer
Dr. Mark A. Niles
North Central Washington Chiropractors Association
Northeast Ohio Academy of Chiropractic
Dr. Tom O'Bryan
Dr. Clair W. O'Dell
Dr. Angela Ornelas
Dr. Kenneth W. Padgett
Palmer College of Chiropractic International Alumni Association
Dr. Michael H. Pardis
Dr. Karl Parker
Dr. Allen Parry
Dr. Donald Pattison
Dr. Gary R. Pennebaker
Dr. Thomas A. Picone
Dr. Robert D. Porter
Dr. James P. Powell
Dr. Leo E. Powell

Dr. Daniel J. Reida
Dr. Francis M. Remedios
Dr. Warren K. Rhodes
Dr. Clark E. Rich
Dr. Cynthia L. Riley
Dr. Eleanor L. Rolnick
Dr. James A. Rosemeyer
Dr. Gary L. Roshy
Dr. Richard Roy
Dr. Larry A. Sabel
Dr. James J. Santiago
Dr. Russell E. Sawyer, Jr.
Dr. Roger Schlade
Dr. Frederick W. Schlueb
Dr. Donald R. Scott
Dr. Mark A. Shaffer
Dr. Miriam C. Shultz
Dr. David Singer
Dr. Allen P. Sipes
Dr. Marilyn P. Smith
Dr. Willard M. Smith
Dr. Roger B. Snyder
Dr. Samuel Soriero
Dr. Brian Sorell
South Dakota Chiropractors Association
Southwestern Ohio Chiropractic Association
Dr. Shannon L. Speer
Dr. Todd E. Spieles
Dr. Louis Sportelli
Dr. Barbara Stanfield
Dr. John D. Stites
Dr. Gary R. Street
Dr. Yoshihiro Suzuki
Dr. John W. Terhune
Dr. William Thimmel
Dr. Danita J. Thomas-Heagy
Dr. Catherine Townsend-Flaherty
Tri-County Chiropractic Association
Dr. Jeffrey Tunick
University du Quebec A Trois-Riveres
University of Natural Healing Arts
Dr. Merv R. Van Engen
Dr. Lance E. Vanderloo
Dr. Sharon Weicman
Dr. Edward C. Williams
Dr. John C. Willis
Dr. A. Joe Willis
Dr. Jerry Ray Willis
Dr. Daryl D. Wills
Dr. Bret Wilson
Dr. Kerwin P. Winkler

Dr. George Winternheimer
Dr. Dennis A. Woggon
Dr. Charles Wood
Dr. Bob Woodward
World Congress of Women Chiropractors
Dr. Gary A. Young
Dr. Frank & Shirley Young
Dr. Henry Zastrow
Dr. Gary A. Zetterberg
Dr. Robert V. Zimmer

## Ruby Sponsors $500

Dr. Dennis A. Acquaro
Dr. Donald R. Acton
Dr. John F. Allenburg
Dr. Franca Alterman
Dr. Frank V. Amatulli
Dr. Wayne Andrews
Dr. Gerald N. Arndt
Dr. Warren & Letha Atkinson
Dr. Joseph Awender
Dr. Birger Baastrup
Dr. Paul R. Bacon
Dr. Debra L. Bader
Dr. Norman J. Bailey
Dr. Eric J. Baker
Dr. Christine P. Baranowski
Dr. Fred H. Barge
Dr. James J. Barile
Dr. H. T. Barnes
Dr. Ercil Victor Beane
Dr. Jeffery G. Beavers
Dr. Christine Bender
Dr. George R. Benichou
Dr. George Benson
Dr. Bonnie Berg-Keehn
Dr. Robert D. Berry
Dr. Wilbur D. Bigler
Dr. Gary R. Billingsley
Dr. Steven Bircher
Dr. Gary D. Black
Dr. Anthony & Barbara Blisko
Dr. David M. Blong
Dr. Harold D. Bobb
Dr. Robert A. Boisvert
Dr. James S. Bowles
Dr. Frank Bowling
Dr. B. Dean Bowman
Dr. Edward Brauwn
Dr. Ronald C. Bray
Dr. Fritz Brodbeck
Dr. Barry N. Burak
Dr. Harry & James E. Burch
Dr. James H. Burnham

Dr. Scott P. Burtis
Dr. Daniel T. Byrne
Dr. Joan Byrne
CA Student Chiropractic Assoc. of Los Angeles College of Chiropractic
Ms. Alana K. Callender
Dr. David Campanelli
Dr. W. Brett Carothers
Dr. J. Stanley Casebere
Central Jersey Chiropractic Society
Dr. Mario Cervino
Dr. William Charschan
Dr. Thomas U. Chasse
Dr. Marc Chasse
Dr. Robert W. Chipman
Dr. Neil Christel
Dr. Michael Clark
Dr. Wayne G. Clough
Dr. Richard W. Cohen
Dr. Philip R. Corthier
Dr. Mark E. Cotney
Dr. Rick Cox
Dr. Joan Craft
Dr. Daniel Crane
Dr. Kenneth L. Cripe
Dr. Paul H. Cronk
Dr. James Curatolo
Mrs. Gloria J. Curry
Dr. Glenn T. Curry
Dr. Maurice Cyr
Dr. Michael L. Darr
Dr. Connie F. Davis
Dr. Mark A. Davis
Dr. Thomas L. Davis
Dr. Donald C. DeFabio
Dr. Patrick DeFrancesco
Dr. Philip M. DePasquale
Dr. John De Sutter
Dr. John D. DiFore
Dr. Allen L. Diercks
Dr. Richard Dietzen
Dr. Jeffrey L. Donay
Dr. Glenn A. Drobot
Dr. Richard Duenas
Dr. Christina M. Dumbadse
Dr. Michael J. Eberle
Dr. James D. Edwards
Dr. Jo Eisman
Dr. Fred Elkins
Dr. Ralph G. Ellenberger
Dr. S. M. Elliott
Dr. Horace Elliott
Dr. Jack Elvidge
Dr. Jerry England
Dr. Vincent J. Erario, Jr.

Dr. Will Evans, Jr.
Dr. Jeffrey W. Falk
Dr. Frank Farkas
Dr. Edmund E. Ferguson
Dr. Peter D. Ferguson
Dr. Jon Ferguson
Finnish Chiropractic Union
Dr. J. Michael Flynn
Dr. Allen Foster
Fox Valley Chiropractic Council
Dr. Barry Freedman
Dr. Ronald D. Fudala
Dr. Garry T. Fuller
Dr. Serge Gagnon
Dr. Nancy Gallagher
Dr. Edward J. Galvin
Dr. Samuel M. Gamber
Dr. Marc Gamerman
Dr. Joseph A. Genco
Dr. Mary Ann Gibbs
Dr. Edwin C. Gibbs
Dr. Kevin Gilbert
Dr. Gregory A. Goffe
Dr. C. W. Gonstead
Dr. M. J. Gonstead
Dr. Chester Graham
Dr. Marc Graham
Dr. Kevin K. Granger
Dr. Alvin C. Graun
Dr. Russell B. Grazier
Dr. Steven M. Green
Dr. James L. Greenwald
Dr. Michael Grego
Dr. Robert Gregory
Dr. Robert E. Griffin
Dr. Lynn E. Griffin
Dr. Rob Gruenenfelder
Dr. Ira Grusback
Dr. Hossein Hamadanchi
Dr. Rhonda Hamilton-Roddy
Dr. Michael Haneline
Dr. Robby Hansen
Dr. John C. Hansen
Dr. Ray T. Hanson
Dr. R.C. Harding
Dr. Stephen A. Harris
Dr. Maureen M. Hayes
Dr. Andrea Hayslip
Dr. Glen A. Heese
Dr. Virginia L. Hernly
Dr. Paul Hetrick
Dr. Peter G. Hill
Dr. Daniel J. Hill

Dr. Eugene L. Hirsch
Dr. Larry D. Hirschy
Dr. Debra A. Hobbs
Dr. James L. Holding
Dr. Craig C. Hollowell
Dr. Clair-Marie Holman
Dr. G. Todd Holubitsky
Dr. Robert J. Homonai
Dr. Lee S. Hudson
Dr. Brett A. Hughes
Dr. Harold T. Hughes
Dr. William J. Huizenga
Dr. Linda G. Hunter
Dr. Michele Imossi
Dr. Trevor Ireland
Dr. Joseph G. Irwin
Dr. Peter Jacelone
Dr. Dixie Ann Jepson
Dr. Harley E. Jewell
Dr. Karl Johnson
Dr. Sadie C. Johnson
Dr. Ralph E. Johnson
Dr. Richard B. Johnson
Dr. Diane Johnson
Dr. Thomas Johnson
Dr. Kenton D. Kainz
Dr. Elana Kaplove-Warner
Dr. Steven D. Katz
Dr. Andrew Keehn
Dr. Ronald G. Kelemen
Dr. E. Lawrence Kelly
Kentuckiana Children's Center
Dr. Mha Atma Kaur Khalsa
Dr. Mark Allen King
Dr. Robert Kleinhan
Dr. Michael J. Klosterman
Dr. Barry Knopp
Dr. Anita V. Knopp
Dr. Jean Koffel
Dr. Andrew Kohler
Dr. Mark A. Korchok
Dr. Joseph Kornfeld
Dr. Deborah Kowalski
Dr. Lori L. Krauss
Dr. Patrick Kunerth
Dr. Randall Kurtz
Dr. Stanmore G. Langford
Dr. Stewart L. Larbell
Dr. K. Wayne Latimer
Dr. Michael G. Law
Dr. Henri Leonard LeBel
Dr. Roy Lewis
Dr. Rick B. Longie
Dr. Thomas Lyons
Dr. Elizabeth Lyons
Dr. Paul A. Mack

Dr. Jeffrey A. Majors
Dr. Glenn Manceaux
Dr. Jack D. Manuele
Dr. Louis Manzolillo
Dr. Denise A. Manzolillo
Dr. Donna Maoloney
Dr. Kurt A. Mariano
Dr. John L. Marth
Dr. Peter Martin
Dr. Pete L. Martin
Dr. Avery N. Martin
Dr. Michael A. Martinez
Dr. David Mauk
Dr. Nancy L. McBride
Dr. J.D. McClary
Dr. Heather McClary
Dr. Mark D. McClure
Dr. Edwin E. McConaughy
Dr. Douglas L. Meints
Dr. Richard C. Meoli
Dr. Andre Merrill
Dr. Kristi Mettler
Dr. Bill Mettler
Dr. Kenneth J. Meyer
Mid-Ohio Chiropractic Association
Dr. Bruce V. Milkint
Mr. Gary M. Mohr
Dr. Denise Montgomery
Dr. James B. Morley
Dr. Samuel L. Morris
Dr. Burl G. Morris
Drs. Thomas & Deborah Mosca
Dr. Mark M. Mullins
Dr. Michael D. Mundy
Dr. David A. Neff
Dr. Serge Nerli
Dr. Daniel Neubauer
New England Chiropractic Council
New York State Chiropractic Association
Dr. Raymond Nietzold
Dr. Dan Nihiser
Northern New Jersey Chiropractic Society
Dr. Alan J. Nunez
Dr. Charles L. O'Dea
Dr. Roger K. Oatman
Dr. Donald W. Olson
Open Door Gallery
Oregon Doctors of Chiropractic
Dr. Lawrence E. Oslay
Dr. Thomas D. Palmer
Dr. Rome Palmer

Palmer College of Chiropractic Alumni Association of California
Palmer College of Chiropractic Auxiliary
Dr. John T. Pantalone
Dr. Richard S. Pasko
Dr. Rand Pellegrino
Dr. Daniel Peltonen
Pennsylvania Chiropractic Society, District 6
Dr. Dean A. Perlman
Dr. Charles J. Peterson
Dr. Charles F. Plante
Dr. H. Dale Poland
Dr. Stephen P. Porcari
Dr. Alan R. Post
Dr. Thomas M. Potigian
Dr. Gary Powell
Dr. Bruce Presnick
Dr. Laura Presnick
Dr. Amy E. Prestas
Dr. Jeffrey A. Przybysz
Dr. Michael Quartararo
Dr. Neil Jay Rabin
Dr. William J. Rademacher
Dr. Stephen D. Ragsdale
Dr. James Raker
Dr. John E. Rasmussen
Dr. Linda A. Rassel
Dr. William E. Rector
Dr. Randy Reed
Dr. & Mrs. John D. Reeder
Dr. James L. Rehberger
Dr. Dennis T. Rehrig
Dr. Jeffrey Reilly
Dr. John E. Reisert
Dr. Neal C. Reising
Dr. Daniel O. Reiter
Dr. Michael A. Remmick
Dr. Paula A. Richard
Dr. Michael J. Riemhofer
Dr. Frances Rinaldi
Dr. Beverly N. Roberts
Dr. Dennis D. Robinson
Dr. Peter J. Rocco
Dr. Raymond F. Roddy
Dr. Gordon M. Rody
Dr. Thomas A. Rofrano
Dr. Allyne R. Rosenthal
Dr. Elizabeth Roth
Dr. Drew Rubin
Dr. Henry M. Rubinstein
Dr. W.A. Rud
Dr. David Runfeldt
Dr. Ronald J. Ruscitti
Dr. Patrick P. Russamano

Dr. Robert A. Russell
Dr. Ronald Saltman
San Mateo County Chiropractic Society
Dr. John Sandoz
Dr. R.L. Savoy
Dr. John J. Sayers
Dr. John J. Sayers, Sr.
Dr. Ted L. Sazdanoff
Dr. Jennifer Scavella
Dr. Lois Ann Schaub
Dr. Yeagues Schettini
Dr. John L. Schimmel
Dr. James A. Schimp
Dr. Ralph W. Schramm
Dr. Tim Schroeder
Dr. Lori Anderson Schultz
Dr. John M. Scott
Dr. Timothy D. Scott
Dr. Catherine Sears
Dr. Kimberly Selir
Dr. Lee M. Semmerling
Dr. Lori J. Sender
Dr. Dan Shain
Dr. Mark S. Shelley
Dr. Alan P. Sherr
Dr. Jeanette M. Sherwood
Dr. Ted L. Shrader
Dr. David J. Sim
Dr. Jerrold J. Simon
Dr. Stephen J. Simonetta
Dr. John Sinnott
Dr. Richard Skiersch
Dr. Kirk Skinner
Dr. Garry J. Smith
Dr. John D. Smith
Dr. Mark S. Smith
Dr. Joel Smooke
Dr. Rick L. Snook
Dr. Kenneth So
Dr. Christopher L. Sorenson
Dr. Samuel R. Souch
Dr. David Spitz
Dr. Ken Spresser
Dr. Rosalynne Stampfes
Dr. John Stanton
Dr. Jeanne R. Staudt
Dr. David Stender
Dr. John H. Stiltner
Dr. Irwin G. Strickland
Dr. Thomas Stroot
Dr. John L. Stump
Dr. Young W. Suh
Dr. Laura A. Swingen
Dr. Brett Tallents
Dr. Larry L. Talley
Dr. Paige Thibodeau

E I Medical
E-Z Bis, Inc.
Earthlite Medical & Health
Equipment
Edutainment, Inc.
Ergomedics, Inc.
Essiac Internation, Resperin
Corporation
Explore
F.C.D.
Foundation for Chiropractic
Education / Research
Fukuda Denshi America
Corporation
Fumia Publications
Futrex, Inc.
Galaxy Enterprises, Inc.
General Design Sign
Company, Inc.
Getting To Know You
H F Hill & Associates
H T Lensgraf Company, Inc.
H W Industries, Inc.
HPSC, Inc.
Hants White
Health Care Class Charts
Health Care manufacturing
Health Products Distributors
Healthmate Infra-Red
Systems
Hill Labratories Co.
Horizon Medical Services,
Inc.
Infinity 2
International Chiropractic
Association
International Waterpillow
Limited
Jardine Group Services
Corporation
Juice Plus
Juice Plus / Big Sky
Marketing
KSI
Kansas Videos The
Krames Communications
Langer Biomechanics
Group, Inc.
Life Chair
Life College of Chiropractic
Life Plus
Living Earth Crafts
Lloyd Table Company
Logan College of
Chiropractic
Los Angeles College of
Chiropractic

MBA, Inc.
MORFAM, Inc.
Maharishi Agurveda
Markson Management
Services
Martin Health Care Products
Mastercare US, Inc.
Medi-Pro Products
Medi-Soft
Medical Diagnosis Imaging
of America
Meredith Communications,
Inc.
Metagenics, Inc.
Monad Corporation
Mosby
Multiplex Stimulator, Ltd.
Murdock Pharmaceutic
Nada - Chair
Nail Masters Professional
National Board of
Chiropractic Examiners
National College of
Chiropractic
National Safety
Neurotron, Inc.
New York Chiropractic
College
Nutri-West
OUM & Associates
Ohio State Chiropractic
Association
Open Door Gallery
Orlando, Joe - Sculptor
Orthofeet, Inc.
Orthopedic Physical
Therapy Products
PHOENIX Corporation
Palmer College Bookstore
Palmer College of
Chiropractic
Palmer College of
Chiropractic West
Parker College of
Chiropractic
Performance Health
Phoenix Biolabs
Phyto-Pharmica
Pie Medical / Leisegang
Prism Diagnostic Labs, Inc.
Pro-Med Products, Inc.
Providence Imaging
Products
Providers Funding Services,
Inc.
Quick Notes, Inc.
Quinton Fitness Equipment
Rich - Mar Corporation
EnriqueRodriquez

Saunders Group The, Inc.
Scrip, Inc.
Serola Biomechanics
Sherman College of Straight
Chiropractic
Shimadzu Medical System
Smith Truss Company
Spinalight, Inc.
Summitt Incustries
Supertech, Inc.
TC Medical, Inc
TPT, Inc.
Tekscan, Inc.
Texas Chiropractic College
Thera-Fit Healthcare
Products
Thera-Pillow
Time Value Corporation
US Tables, Inc.
Universal Imaging, Inc.
University of Bridgeport
College of Chiropractic
VF - Works, Inc
Visual Odyssey, Inc.
Vita-Mix Corporation
Vitamin Factory The, Inc.
W. B. Saunders Company
Western States Chiropractic
College
Whitehall Manufacturing
Williams & Wilkins
Williams Healthcare Systems

## STATE, COUNTRY, PROVINCIAL, AND SPECIAL ASSOCIATION MEMBERS

### STATE MEMBER $1250

Alabama Chiropractic
Council
Alabama State Chiropractic
Association
Alaska Chiropractic Society
Arizona Association of
Chiropractic
Arkansas Chiropractic
Association
California Chiropractic
Association
Chiropractic Association of
Ohio

Colorado Chiropractic
Association
Connecticut Chiropractic
Association
Connecticut Chiropractic
Council

Delaware Chiropractic
Society
Florida Chiropractic
Association
Florida Chiropractic Society
Georgia Chiropractic
Association
Georgia Council of
Chiropractic
Hawaii State Chiropractic
Association
Idaho Association of
Chiropractic Physicians
Illinois Chiropractic Society
Illinois Prarie State
Chiropractic Association
Indiana International
Chiropractors Association
Indiana State Chiropractic
Association
Iowa Chiropractic Society
Kansas Chiropractic
Association
Kentucky Association of
Chiropractors
Kentucky Chiropractic
Society
Louisianna Chiropractic
Association
Maine Chiropractic
Association
Maryland Chiropractic
Association
Massachusetts Chiropractic
Society
Michigan Chiropractic
Council
Michigan Chiropractic
Society
Minnesota Chiropractic
Association
Mississippi Associated
Chiropractors
Missouri State Chiropractors
Association
Montana Chiropractic
Physiotherapy Council
Nebraska Chiropractic
Physicians Association
New Hampshire Straight
Chiropractic Society
New Jersey Chiropractic
Society
New Jersey Council of
Chiropractic
New Mexico Chiropractic
Association
New York Chiropractic
Council

New York State
Chiropractic Association
North Carolina Chiropractic
Association
North Dakota Chiropractic
Association
Ohio State Chiropractic
Association
Oklahoma State
Chiropractic Association
Oregon Chiropractic
Association
Pennsylvania Chiropractic
Society
Rhode Island Chiropractic
Society
South Carolina Chiropractic
Association
South Dakota Chiropractors
Association
Tennessee Chiropractic
Association
Texas Chiropractic
Association
Virginia Chiropractic
Association
Washington State
Chiropractic Association
Washington, D.C.
Chiropractic Association
West Virginia Chiropractic
Society
Wisconsin Chiropractic
Association

### SPECIAL ASSOCIATIONS $1250

Academy for the General
Practice of Chiropractic
American Black
Chiropractic Association
Chiropractic Rehabilitation
Association
Congress of Chiropractic
State Associations
Consortium for
Chiropractic Research
Federation of Straight
Chiropractic Organizations
Kale Foundation
Lincoln College Education
and Research Fund
Miami Valley Chiropractic
Society, 8th District of
OSCA
National Association of
Chiropractic Attorneys
New York Chiropractic
College Alumni Association

## SPECIAL ASSOCIATIONS $1250 (Cont.)

North Carolina Palmer College of Chiropractic Alumni Association
Palmer College of Chiropractic International Alumni Association
Palmer College of Chiropractic - West International Alumni Association
Palmer College of Chiropractic Alumni Association of California
San Diege County Chiropractic Health Foundation
Shelby County Chiropractic Association
South Pudget Sound Chiropractic Association & Dr. Keith Innes
Tennessee Valley Chiropractic Association

## PROVINCIAL ASSOCIATION MEMBER $1250

Association des Chiropracticiens du Quebec

## COUNTRY ASSOCIATION $1250

Asocicion Espanola de Quiropractica
Association des Chiropraticiens de France
Association of Swiss Chiropractors
British Chiropractic Association
Canadian Chiropractic Association
Chiropractic Council of Japan
Chiropractors' Association of Australia
Colegio de Profesionistas Cientifico Quiropracticos de Mexico
Japanese Chiropractic Association
Korean Chiropractic Association
New Zealand Chiropractors' Association
Norwegian Chiropractors' Association

## DOCUMENTARY AIRING DONORS

### $300,000 Donation
Dr. William Harris

### $32,000 Donation
National Chiropractic Mutual Insurance Company

### $25,000 Donation
Life College of Chiropractic Educational Funding Services
Association of Chiropractic Colleges

### $20,000 Donation
FootLevelers

### $5,000 - $9,999 Donors
Dr. David J. Below
Connecticut Chiropractic Council
Dr. Luigi DiRubba
Markson Management Services

### $2,000 - $4,999 Donors
Anrig Chiropractic Offices
Dr. Darrell E. Atchley
Dr. Nancy A. Cappiello
Dr. Gerard W. Clum
Drs. David & Cheryl Coates
Dr. Norman J. Gloekler
Dr. & Mrs. Robert & Jeanine Graykowski
Dr. John P. Grumish
Dr. John & Judy Hinwood
Dr. Ernest Laubach
Dr. John D. Lockenour
Dr. Frank Meisel
Dr. Dennis Paustian
Dr. & Mrs. Russel W. Pavkov
Dr. Tom Perrault
Drs. Paul & Imogene Protz
Dr. Cathy A. Riekeman
Royal Chiropractic Knights of the Round Table
Dr. Fredrick R. Santangelo
Dr. Selina Sigafoose-Jackson
Dr. David Stender
Susquehanna Association of Chiropractic Education
Dr. Gary Walsemann

### $1,000 - $1,999 Donors
Dr. Robert A. Abbruzzese

Dr. Joe Accurso
Dr. Gerald J. Agasar
Dr. Franca Alterman
Dr. Kevin B. Amen
Dr. Darcey Andersen
Dr. Claudia Anrig
Dr. Susi M. Anrig
Dr. Josef Arnould
Dr. Marvin Arnsdorff
Dr. Ayla Azad
Dr. John Babich
Dr. Greg Baker
Bakke Family Chiropractors
Drs. Steven & Terresa Balestracci
Drs. Carol & Joseph Ball
Dr. James J. Barile
Dr. Joseph V. Barile
Dr. Jack M. Barton
Dr. Richard Barwell
Dr. Donald Baune
Dr. Ercil Victor Beane
Drs. Gregory & Christine Beasley
Dr. Teshna Beaulieu
Dr. Dennis Becklund
Dr. George R. Benichou
Drs. Mary Ann & Robert Benson
Dr. David M. Bentz
Dr. Linda Berry
Dr. Edwin D. Berry II
Dr. Gary Beytin
Dr. Howard J. Boos
Dr. Annette Bourdon
Dr. Lauren Bourgeois
Dr. Robert Braile
Dr. Morris Braum
Dr. Erich Breitenmoser
Broderick Family
Dr. & Mrs. Allen W. Bronson
Dr. Jean Brown
Dr. Michael A. Bruns
Dr. Brenda K. Buckley
Dr. Lynn Buhr
Dr. & Mrs. Robert Buis
Dr. Joseph L. Burns
Dr. Scott P. Burtis
Dr. David Cahill
Dr. George A. Camacho
Dr. Louis S. Carr
Dr. Marcia Cerutty
Dr. Mitchell S. Chambers
Dr. Sanford Chapnick
Dr. Michael Chimes, Jr.
Dr. Christopher J. Cianci
Dr. Frank & Katherine Cicirello

Dr. Betty Ciuchta
Dr. Carl Cleveland III
Dr. Chris Coffman
Dr. Howard Cohn
Dr. Larry Cole
Dr. John B. Conca
Contra Costa Chiropractic Society
Dr. Dennis Cozzocrea
Dr. Bruce Crabtree
Dr. Kenneth Csillag
Dr. Jeffrey M. Culbert
Dr. Rodney L. Cummings
Dr. Terry R. Custer
Dr. Randy Daird
Dr. Lance & Sherry Darrett
Dr. Eugene Davidson
Dr. Steve A. DeShaw
Dr. Stephen A. Dean
Dee Cee Laboratories, Inc.
Dr. Fred P. Dehn
Dr. Carl F. Dieter
Dr. Brad Double
Drs. Tom & Nancy Dunlap
Dr. Craig Dykgraaf
Drs. Lance & Sherry Durrett
Dr. Gary F. Edwards
Dr. John Edwards
Dr. Barry L. Ellin
Dr. William C. Eriksen
Dr. Elizabeth R. Erkenswick
Dr. Bryan R. Errico
Dr. Ronald J. Farabaugh
Dr. Brenda Faulkner
Dr. Mary Ann Fensterbusch
Dr. Edmund E. Ferguson
Dr. Jon Ferguson
Dr. Sharon L. Fitelson
Dr. Troy E. Fluent
Dr. J. Michael Flynn
Dr. Judy A. Forester
Dr. Evelyn Forrester
Four State Chiropractic Association
Dr. Dale Frack
Dr. Luraghi Francesca
Dr. Diana C. Frasier
Dr. Angela Gambale
Dr. Stephen & William Garnett
Dr. James P. Garrett
Dr. Phillip Gawthrop
Dr. Michele K. Gerard
Dr. Harley D. Gilthvedt
Dr. Asya Ginzburg-Levin
Dr. Joseph T. Goben
Dr. Nelson T. Goff
Dr. Roger M. Goodheart

Dr. Billy D. Grant
Dr. John L. Grant
Dr. Russell B. Grazier
Dr. J.L. Green
Dr. Doug S. Greenspan
Dr. Cindy Guillett
Dr. Bruce C. Hagen
Drs. Greg & Melanie Hawthorne
Dr. David Hendrey
Dr. Bradley Hennen
Dr. Clifford J. Hochberg
Dr. Johanna M. Hoeller
Dr. Bob Hoffman
Dr. David Hoffman
Dr. Stuart Hoffman
Dr. William F. Holmberg
Dr. & Mrs. John & Josee Homza
Dr. Thomas R. Horn
Dr. Dominique Hort
Dr. Mark Houk
Dr. Douglas K. Howell
Dr. Diana Hudgins
Dr. Dallas D. Humble
Dr. Richard Irby
Drs. Bruce & Anita Jackson
Dr. Kevin Jackson
Dr. Bill & Peg Johnson
Dr. & Mrs. David W. Johnson
Dr. Karl R.O.S. Johnson
Dr. Lars Johnson
Dr. Karl M. Jordan
Dr. Ken Jordan
Dr. Palmera Kabana
Dr. Lloyd Katz
Dr. Pamela Kirkwood
Dr. William Kneebone
Drs. Jeane & Jack Koenen
Drs. John & Laura Kosbau
Drs. Diane & Gerard Kramer
Dr. Edward Kramer, Jr.
Dr. Alan Kunkel, Jr
Dr. & Mrs. Henri LeBel
Dr. Lynn LeBel
Dr. Stephanie Leonard
Dr. Sharon Leonardo-Barone
Dr. Ben Lerner
Dr. & Mrs. Kasey Lewis
Life College
Dr. Teresa H. Litchfield
Dr. James M. Loftus
Dr. Patricia Lorence
Dr. Timothy W. Love

Dr. Lance & Valerie Lorfeld
Dr. Kevin Lowey
Dr. Scott M. Lund
Dr. Scott B. Macaulay
Dr. Mary Madden
Dr. John P. Maher
Dr. Carol A. Malizia
Dr. Jack D. Manuele
Dr. H. Markovitz
Dr. Avery N. Martin
Dr. Peter Martin
Dr. S. Scott Matz
Dr. Melinda Maxwell
Dr. Sam McCaslin
Drs. John & Jan McKay
Dr. Bruce A. McKillican
Dr. Rick McMichael
Drs. David & Lorraine
    Melendez
Dr. & Mrs. Mark Meleski
Dr. & Mrs. Ron Meola
Michigan Chiropractic
    Society, Inc.
Dr. Denise Montgomery
Dr. & Mrs. Ben Morgan
Dr. Daniel H. Moriarty
Dr. Morgan P. Mullican
Dr. S.A. Mueller
Dr. Rick Mustain
Dr. Phil Nadler
Dr. Brian J. Nantais
New Zealand Chiropractors
    Association
Dr. Dan Nihiser
Dr. Heather Norman
Northern New Jersey
    Chiropractic Society, Inc.
North Shore Chiropractic
    Society
Dr. Russell O'Neill
Dr. Rene Oehlenschlaeger
Dr. Jonathan W. Olson
Dr. Nicholas G. Opie
Dr. Bruce A. Owers
Mr. Larry Patten
Mr. Michael Penn
Dr. Steven M. Perman
Dr. Gary Petry
Princeton Chiropractic
    Center
Dr. H. Dale Poland
Dr. James P. Powell
Dr. Tom & Shelley Preston
Dr. & Mrs. Chris Quigley
Dr. Nancy Radigan

Dr. Dori Rammelsberg-
    Dvorak
Dr. Joe Ranney
Dr. Linda A. Rassel
Dr. Cynthia Ratkowski
Dr. Bradley J. Reich
Dr. Max Reinecke
Dr. Francis M. Remedios
Dr. Gary Rettig
Dr. Curt Rexroth
Dr. Heather Rice
Dr. Paul Riegleman
Dr. Steven Riggleman
Drs. Kathleen & Gordon
    Rixon
Dr. Richard Rizzuto
Dr. Thomas C. Roballey
Dr. Glen A. Robison
Dr. Peter Rohrs
Dr. James Rosemeyer
Dr. Scott Rosenthal
Dr. Gary L. Roshy
Dr. Raymond Roy
Dr. Kenneth Ruf
Dr. Mary Lou Sackett-Penn
Dr. Thomas Salmon
Dr. Stephen Saunders
Drs. Joseph & Katherine
    Schlaffer
Dr. Wayne E. Schmidt
Ms. Annie Schmitt
Drs. Connie & David
    Schroder
Dr. William G. Schroeder
Dr. Sandra S. Schwartz
Dr. Nancy K. Shaler
Dr. Jeffrey N. Shebovsky
Dr. Shawn Sheridan
Dr. Terry L. Shull
Dr. Anthony P. Siano, Jr.
Dr. Nancy C. Smith
Ms. Suzanne Smith
Dr. Paula J. Sperry
Dr. Todd E. Spieles
Dr. Lawrence E. Srnold
Dr. Charles R. Stanfield
Dr. Greg Stetzel
Dr. John D. Stites
Dr. Steven S. Stryker
Dr. Mark Swain
Dr. Robin G. Taylor
Dr. Erik Thompson
Dr. Pamela Thompson
Dr. Sondara Tillou
Dr. Kathy Tomsich-Evans
Dr. Stephen Tranter
Dr. Steve Troeger
Dr. Jan Van Beelen

Dr. Brian A. Varga
Dr. Marc A. Weinberg
Dr. Mindy A. Weingarten
Dr. Don M. Weiss
Dr. Linda DiMauro Wells
Dr. Peter Wells
Dr. John M. Wertin
Dr. Gerald L. Whalen
Dr. Ingrid E. White
Drs. Troy & Sara Wierman
Dr. Sheila Q. Williams
Dr. Daryl D. Wills
Dr. Joe Wilson
Dr. Roger & Alison Wilson
Dr. C.H. Winkler
Dr. David M. Winsor
Dr. Joan Winters
Dr. William F. Winters
Dr. Thomas A. Wong
Dr. Ron Wuest
Dr. Thomas Zorich

**$100 - $499 Donors**
Dr. Marianne Abate
Dr. Lyle Abbas
Dr. Duane R. Abbe
Dr. Donald R. Acton
Drs. Susan & Kurt Adams
Dr. Greg Adams
Dr. Darl D. Albrecht
Dr. Bruce D. Aldrich
Ms. Cheyl H. Alexson
Dr. Thomas J. Allen
Dr. Gary J. Alves
Dr. Anthony P. Amato
Dr. Laura R. Ames
Dr. Ken Anderson
Dr. Herbert C. Anderson
Dr. Bart Anderson
Dr. George Anthon, Jr.
Dr. Leo S. Arcand
Dr. Stephen E. Armstrong
Dr. Gerald N. Arndt
Drs. Dennis & Kara Arne
Dr. Glenn Askedall
Dr. Lisa L. Aston
Dr. Lyman S. Atchley
Dr. Warren & Letha
    Atkinson
Dr. William Auderman
Dr. A. Anthony Avedisian
Mr. Daniel Aviv
Dr. Brett Axelrod
Dr. O.W. Babcock
Dr. Robert Babriel
Dr. Stanley N. Bacso
Dr. Paul Baker
Dr. Debbie Baker

Dr. Patrick Baker
Ms. Stasi & Kristyn Bara
Dr. Andrew M. Barkin
Dr. James Barnes
Dr. Spencer H. Baron
Dr. L.E. Barrows
Dr. Kevin R. Barry
Dr. & Mrs. Michael J. Bartell
Drs. Paul & Barbara Basile
Dr. Steven M. Basler
Dr. Kathy L. Basler
Dr. D. Michael Battey
Dr. Charles E. Baxter
Dr. Scott Beavers
Dr. Jeffery G. Beavers
Ms. Jennifer Beck
Dr. Timoghy A. Belanger
Dr. Garry Bell
Dr. Daniel W. Bell
Dr. D. Richard Bellamy
Dr. Kathleen Bente
Dr. Lori L. Bents
Dr. Robert C. Bergeron
Dr. Gene A. Bergmann
Dr. Mark A. Bianchi
Dr. John Biss
Dr. Gary D. Black
Dr. Michael P. Blackman
Dr. G. Lansing Blackshaw
Dr. Martin R. Blanchard, Jr.
Bodle Chiropractic
Dr. Nick Bogannam
Dr. Timothy W. Bogren
Dr. Robert S. Bolsand
Dr. Grant Bond
Dr. David P. Bourree
Dr. James H. Bowen
Dr. J. Leigh Bower
Dr. David Boyd
Dr. Patrick Boykin
Dr. Donald Bradley
Dr. James T. Brady
Dr. William X. Bratcher
Dr. Marvin Braun
Dr. Marlin Braun
Drs. Michael & Karen
    Brennan
Dr. Loren M. Brett
Dr. John Bricker
Dr. Russell D. Broccoli
Dr. S.J. Brodar
Dr. Lance E. Brooks
Dr. Donald L. Brooks
Dr. Ken Brough
Dr. Randall L. Brown
Dr. Richard L. Brown
Dr. Elena Brown
Dr. Kirk Brown

Dr. Mark A. Brown
Drs. Barry & Ogla Silva
    Bryan
Dr. John Bueler, Jr.
Dr. A.F. Bugai
Dr. Craig F. Buhler
Dr. Kerry E. Bulman
Dr. Ralph Burris
Dr. Anthony A. Cacioppo
Dr. Rick Calcara
California Student
    Chiropractic Association
Dr. Michael E. Camerer
Dr. Richard W. Campbell
Dr. Michael A. Capogna
Dr. Brett D. Cardonick
Dr. Marty Caron
Dr. Matthew R. Caron
Dr. William Carone
Dr. Timothy M. Casey
Dr. & Mrs. James Cassillo
Dr. Gerard R. Cassista
Dr. Jeanne E. Castellucci
Dr. Rick Cavallaro
Dr. Mario Cervino
Dr. Marc Chasse
Dr. Robert D. Chatfield
Dr. Lawrence Clayman
Dr. Mary M. Cheboski
Dr. Gil Chimes
Dr. Jeffrey J. Ciarlelli
Dr. Michael Clancey
Dr. Michael T. Clark
Dr. Lewis M. Clark
Dr. Kathleen M. Clark
Dr. Mark T. Clark
Dr. Carolyn F. Clauss
Dr. Laurette Clowes
Dr. Don C. Clum
Dr. Jean E. Cohen
Dr. Richard Cohen
Dr. Don E. Cole
Dr. Gina Colucci
Dr. Herbert F. Congram
Dr. Mary M. Conners
Dr. Donald S. Cook
Dr. William E. Copes
Dr. Gerald F. Coppola, Jr.
Drs. Brett & Anne Marie
    Coryell
Dr. Charles Cottier
Ms. Diane K. Coulter
Dr. Victoria Couluris
Mr. Casey Crisp
Dr. Michael P. Crouchley
Dr. L.H. Crow
Dr. J. Murphy Crum
Dr. Miguel Cruz

Dr. Dennis Cummins
Dr. Bruce Cupp
Dr. Anthony Curcio
Dr. Maurice Cyr
Dr. Jeannette M. Czerwiecki
Dr. Rodolfo A. Dabalos
Dr. Rodney J. Dahlinger
Dr. Berthol J. Daigle
Dr. Larry W. Danser
Dr. Rick Davis
Dr. & Mrs. Alan Davis
Dr. Lloyd S. Davis
Dr. Glen Davis
Dr. Orrin E. Davis
Dr. David J. Day
Dr. Dennis J. DeLoretta
Dr. Charles L. DeMarco
Dr. John P. Degenhart
Mr. Jason Deitch
Dr. John J. Dematte
Dr. & Mrs. Allen Deprey
Dr. Dennis P. Derocher
Dr. Sonya DiDomenico
Dr. & Mrs. Rick DiGregorio
Dr. & Mrs. Douglas DiSiena
Dr. Francis A. Dia
Dr. Brett Diaz
Dr. Paula Dimaio
Dr. Guy F. Dionne
Drs. Jerry & Ganelle Dippe
Dr. Mark K. Dollinger
Mrs. Lois Donnelly
Dr. John C. Doriss
Dr. Bert DuVal
Dr. F. Marcus Dunn
Dr. Lori Anne Dunn
Dr. Kathleen Dvorak
Dr. Terry H. Eagle
Dr. Catherine S. Ebalo
Dr. Ken D. Edgar
Dr. Paul R. Edwards
Dr. Richard Edwards
Dr. Wayne R. Eiban
Dr. Charles W. Eisenhuth
Mr. Ed Elbrecht
Dr. Ralph G. Ellenberger
Dr. Jack Elvidge
Ms. Christy Emerson
Dr. Terrance E. Erdman
Dr. Loren Ernst
Dr. Adrienne Fabrizio
Dr. Catherine M. Falk
Dr. Andrew Farrago

Dr. William L. Fausett
Dr. William P. Feiring
Dr. Mark Feldman
Dr. A.J. Ferelle
Dr. Juan Ferry
Dr. Adam Fidel
Dr. Ray E. Finegan
Dr. Stephen C. Finn
Dr. Jerald Flinn
Dr. Charles L. Foster
Dr. Darcy K. Fox
Dr. Joseph Frasco
Dr. Brad Fraum
Dr. Tim W. Fuehrer
Dr. Marc A. Fulkerson
Dr. Garry T. Fuller
Dr. John Funnell
Dr. Glenn Gaberi
Dr. Martin C. Gage
Dr. Michael J. Gagnon
Dr. John Gantner
Dr. Eugene Gehrau
Dr. Linda Gent
Dr. Thomas J. Georges
Drs. Marcy & Dean Gerads
Dr. Thomas J. Gerau
Dr. Russell W. Gibbons
Dr. David L. Gilbertson
Dr. Michael R. Girard
Dr. R. Tyler Given
Dr. Steven Gleue
Dr. Anne Glouse
Dr. H. John Goebel
Drs. Arnold & Rita Goldman
Dr. Pedro Gonzalez
Dr. Gary Goodell
Dr. David I. Graber
Dr. John Graham
Dr. Chester Graham
Dr. Stephen A. Grande
Dr. Alvin C. Graun
Dr. James A. Gray
Dr. Richard L. Green
Dr. Richard W. Greendyk
Dr. Paul S. Gregory
Dr. James P. Groene
Dr. John Grone
Dr. A.B. Groos
Dr. Craig D. Gruber
Dr. Martin Gruder
Dr. Rob Gruenenfelder
Dr. Ira Grusback
Dr. R.C. Hadley
Dr. Richard W. Hall
Dr. Eugene Z. Haller

Drs. Christopher & Jill Halligan
Dr. Rehana Hamid
Dr. Laron L. Hardy
Dr. Nader Harerchan
Dr. Kirk Harmon
Dr. & Mrs. Dennis & Stacy Harris
Dr. Don & Sang Harrison
Dr. Patrick Hart
Dr. Donald W. Haspel
Dr. & Mrs. George Heathcote
Dr. Dale E. Heil
Dr. Derrick Hendricks
Dr. Hartley H. Hennessey
Dr. Kiki Herfert
Dr. & Mrs. W. Curtis & Kelly Herwig
Dr. Gregory J. Hicks
Dr. James Hinsch
Dr. James Hirning
Dr. Don Hirsh
Dr. Glenn J. Hoffman
Dr. Ellen M. Hoffman
Dr. G. Todd Holubitsky
Dr. Deborah Hoolahan
Dr. Stuart M. Horen
Dr. Corrie E. Horshinski
Dr. Lloyd A. Horton
Dr. & Mrs. David & Marjorie Howells
Dr. Leo C. Huddleston
Dr. Eliot Hudes
Dr. Rita & Michael Hughes
Ms. Phyllis Hughes
Dr. William J. Huizenga
Dr. Gary Hutchinson
Dr. Peter A. Hyatt
Dr. David Israel
Dr. Ken Iwaki
Dr. Walter S. Jaakkola
Dr. Peter Jacelone
Dr. Bent Jacobsen
Dr. Thomas V. Jacques, PSC
Dr. Patricia Jamison
Dr. Jean Jenkins
Dr. Dermot Jinks
Dr. John P. Johnson
Dr. Cindy Johnson
Dr. & Mrs. Gordon & Carol Johnson
Dr. John M. Johnsrud
Dr. Paul F. Johnston
Dr. John S. Jordan
Dr. Joseph M. Juliano
Dr. Wendy Kagan

Dr. Arlene Kahn
Dr. Albert R. Kalter
Dr. Patricia Kampfer
Dr. Stanley S. Kaplan
Dr. Timothy Kaufmann
Dr. Douglas Kaul
Dr. Julie Kawnt
Dr. John H. Keefe, III
Keehn Chiropractic Office
Dr. Allan G. Keller
Dr. & Mrs. Bruce Kesten
Dr. Mark A. Kestner
Dr. Shakati S. Khalsa
Dr. Leon King
Dr. Andrew C. Kirk
Dr. Arthur Klein
Mr. & Mrs. Greg & Nancy Klepetka
Dr. David Klinda
Dr. Casey Kobylinski
Dr. Kenneth H. Koenig
Dr. David Koffman
Dr. Tadamasa Kohayashi
Dr. Todd B. Kohout
Ms. Jeffra L. Korell
Dr. Mark B. Kossian
Dr. Michael J. Kostas
Dr. Paul A. Kowacki
Dr. James C. Kreger
Dr. David O. Krenek
Dr. Christine M. Krsko
Dr. J.P. Krueger
Dr. Rodney P. Kruse
Dr. Paul J. Krynen
Dr. Barbara A. Kunkle
Dr. Jean Lachance
Dr. Kathleen M. Lamack
Dr. Karl L. Lamb
Dr. Ken & Vanessa Lamechick
Dr. Charles A. Lantz
Dr. K. Wayne Latimer
Dr. Beau S. Lawyer
Dr. & Mrs. Russ & Darlene LeBlonc
Dr. Chun Woo Lee
Dr. Asher Leeder
Drs. Virginia & Gerard Legault
Dr. James J. Lehman
Dr. Jonathan Leibell
Dr. George Lentini
Dr. Rose Lepien
Dr. Neal Lepovetsky
Dr. Erik Lerner
Dr. Howard J. Levinson

Life Chiropractic College – West
Dr. Kenneth L. Lim
Dr. Thomas Linden
Dr. Debby Lipka
Dr. Patrick Llama
Dr. & Mrs. Stuart Lockwood
Dr. Stewart S. Loeb
Dr. Paul M. Lombardi
Dr. David Lombardi
Dr. Carol Ann Lotito
Dr. Kevin J. Loughlin
Dr. & Mrs. Roy M. Love
Dr. C.H. Lundahl
Dr. Judith K. Luongo
Dr. Louis Lupinacci
Dr. Maura C. Lyddy
Drs. Mikel & Patricia Lydy
Dr. Russell MacDonald
Dr. Dana MacPhee
Dr. Michael W. Macleod
Dr. John A. Macrone
Dr. Patrick S. Maddigan
Dr. Glen D. Madsen
Dr. Carol M. Mahoney
Dr. Daniel E. Maiman
Dr. Gregory S. Malakoff
Dr. Victoria Malchar
Dr. Matthew J. Mallen
Dr. Cacinda L. Maloney
Dr. John Maltese
Dr. Nalyn Russo Marcus
Dr. Dennis Mariano
Dr. Gina M. Marino
Dr. Jack Markey
Dr. J. Adam Martin, Jr.
Dr. Margaret M. Martinez
Dr. Joseph J. Martini
Dr. Philip R. Martino
Dr. Charles E. Masarsky
Dr. Irvin Mathias
Dr. Michael Matury
Dr. Richard L. Mauro
Dr. Dale May
Dr. Terry McCoskey
Dr. Lyle E. McFadden
Dr. Eileen McGough
Dr. Michael S. McKelvey
Dr. Charles W. McNeal
Dr. Marc Meier
Dr. Ferdinand Mejilla
Dr. Linda M. Meola
Dr. Richard C. Meoli
Dr. Brad Merritt
Dr. Daniel A. Michalec
Dr. Eric S. Mininsohn

160

## BOOK PURCHASE
(Cont.)

Dr. Robert R. Anderson
Dr. Kendall D. Anderson
Dr. Michael J. Anderson
Dr. Sherry L. Anderson
Dr. Eric W. Anderson
Dr. Kasper Andresen
Dr. Linda M. Andrews
Dr. Jeffrey Angelli
Dr. Krishna Anmolsingh
Dr. Susie M. Anrig
Dr. Claudia A. Anrig
Dr. Daniel Anrig
Dr. Ernst Anrig
Dr. Pal Apall
Dr. Steve Apicerno
Dr. Aaron Applebaum
Dr. Benoit G. Archambeau
Dr. Alfie Arcidiacono
Dr. Sophia Argeropoulos
Dr. Joseph F. Arme
Dr. David W. Armor
Dr. Stephen E. Armstrong
Dr. Gerald N. Arndt
Dr. Marvin T. Arnsdorff
Dr. Cynthia Arp
Dr. Sonali Asrani
Dr. Glenn J. Asti
Dr. Darrell E. Atchley
Dr. Peter R. Atkins
Dr. Warren B. Atkinson
Dr. William D. Aukerman
Dr. Gunn Austlid
Dr. Joseph Awender
Dr. Michel A. Aymon
Dr. Birger Baastrup
Dr. Mary L. Babian
Dr. John Babich
Dr. Bonnie Baclawski
Dr. Paul R. Bacon
Dr. James J. Badge
Dr. George S. Baer
Dr. Russell R. Baerwaldt
Dr. Herbert F. Bahr
Dr. Norman J. Bailey
Dr. Ronald G. Baker
Dr. Mark A. Baker
Dr. Gregory A. Baker
Dr. Michael P. Baker
Dr. Roger Baker
Dr. R. Douglas Baker
Dr. Deborah B. Baker
Baker & Taylor Books
Dr. Meredith H. Bakke
Dr. Howard A. Balduc
Dr. Therese Balestracci

Dr. Steven Balestracci
Dr. Carol L. Ball
Dr. Joseph R. Ball
Dr. William D. Balla
Dr. Herman L. Ballard
Dr. Terumi Bando
Dr. Gary L. Baney
Dr. George P. Banitch
Dr. Scott J. Banks
Dr. Stephen J. Bardsley
Dr. Christopher J. Barham
Dr. Joseph V. Barile
Dr. H.T. Barnes
Dr. Edward J. Barrington
Dr. Daniele A. Bartamini
Dr. Michael J. Bartell
Dr. Ronald J. Barth
Dr. Marion C. Barto
Dr. Charles L. Bartoli
Dr. Jack M. Barton
Dr. Stephen Barton
Dr. Richard G. Barwell
Dr. Regis M. Barwin
Dr. Steven Basler
Dr. Mary Basler
Dr. Anthony V. Bastecki
Dr. Keith C. Bastian
Dr. Luke Bastian
Dr. Edward M. Bateson
Dr. Blair Bauer
Dr. Iris Baumann
Dr. Donald J. Baune
Dr. Ramin Bayani
Dr. William R. Bazin
Dr. Ercil V. Beane
Dr. Herbert M. Beatty
Dr. Scott Beavers
Dr. Jeffrey G. Beavers
Dr. Gregory J. Becco
Dr. Dennis G. Becklund
Dr. Michael A. Beddoe
Dr. Ronald P. Beideman
Dr. Bernard Belanger
Dr. David S. Belknap
Dr. John P. Bellomo
Dr. Leslie W. Bellwood, Jr.
Dr. David J. Below
Dr. Frank C. Bemis
Dr. George R. Benichou
Dr. Dale J. Bennett
Dr. Steven Bennett
Dr. Mary Ann Benson
Dr. Robert J. Benson
Dr. Lori L. Bents
Dr. Karen E. Berger
Dr. Ronald D. Berju
Dr. Christine A. Berju

Dr. Craig Berko
Dr. Robert Berkowitz
Dr. Breillat Bernard
Dr. Robert D. Berry
Dr. Linda Berry
Dr. Edwin D. Berry II
Dr. Michael Beyer
Dr. David G. Biby
Dr. Wilbur D. Bigler
Dr. Mark A. Bilan
Dr. Stephen D. Billings
Dr. Gary R. Billingsley
Dr. Carol Billingsley
Dr. Joseph F. Binkley
Dr. Janice Bird
Dr. Joseph C. Birdwell
Dr. Margaret C. Bishop
Dr. Eirik Bjargo
Dr. K. Bjodstrup Kristensen
Dr. Christopher Black
Dr. Michael P. Blackman
Blackwell North American,
    Inc.
Dr. Oliver R. Blaker
Dr. William K. Blaker
Dr. Tom Blakkisrud
Dr. Jerry D. Blanchard
Dr. David M. Blong
Dr. Harold D. Bobb
Dr. Michael J. Bodle
Dr. Nicholas S. Bogannam
Dr. Roland E. Bohemier
Dr. Brett D. Bolton
Dr. Rod P. Bonello
Dr. George P. Bonner
Books Aplenty
Dr. Howard J. Boos
Dr. James R. Boots
Dr. Martin J. Borge
Dr. Raymond E. Boring
Dr. Alonzo Borja
Dr. William H. Boshoff
Dr. Annette A. Bourdon
Dr. Gary J. Bourdon
Dr. David P. Bourree
Dr. Sally A. Bowen
Dr. Ben Bowers
Dr. Kay R. Bowher
Dr. James S. Bowles
Dr. David R. Boyd
Dr. Stephen C. Boyd
Dr. John Boyden II
Dr. Joseph N. Brace
Dr. Robert Braile
Dr. Rodney W.
    Brandenburger
Dr. Martin Brantner

Dr. Torsten G. Braun
Dr. Roy T. Breen
Dr. William G. Breitenbach
Dr. Erich Breitenmoser
Dr. Kathy Brendlinger
Dr. Michael T. Breneman
Dr. Michael S. Brennan
Dr. John B. Bricker
Dr. Gordon R. Brinsmead
Dr. Daniel Britt
Dr. A. Charles Bro
Dr. James L. Brockhohn
Dr. Jeffrey L. Brockman
Dr. Friedrich A. Brodbeck
Dr. Gerald R. Broderick
Dr. Donald G. Broman
Dr. Julie Brons
Dr. Allen Bronson
Dr. Robert T. Brooks
Dr. Thomas J. Brophy
Dr. Chris D. Brosnahan
Dr. Ken D. Brough
Dr. Stephen Brower
Dr. Jeffrey W. Brower
Dr. Darvin L. Brown
Dr. Howard J. Brown
Dr. Brian J. Brown
Dr. Mikel R. Brown
Dr. Brenda Brown
Dr. Katherine Brown-Flesia
Dr. Arlo R. Brownlie
Dr. Margaret Brownlie
Dr. Michael Bruno
Dr. Michael A. Bruns
Dr. Florian Brunstein
Dr. Thomas Bryant
Dr. Peter Bryner
Dr. Ronald R. Bubel
Dr. Craig E. Buchanan
Dr. Robert G. Buckley
Dr. Kevin Bugg
Dr. Leif Bugge-Aaroe
Dr. Lynn Buhr
Dr. Robert Buis
Dr. Peter W. Bull
Dr. Jeffrey E. Buller
Dr. Jerry J. Bullough
Dr. Jeffrey G. Buntrock
Dr. Harry E. Burch
Dr. Susan G. Burger
Dr. Phyllis M. Burgio
Dr. Joel Burkett
Dr. Gordon Burkholder
Dr. J. Richard Burns
Dr. Mickey G. Burt
Dr. Scott P. Burtis
Dr. Joanne Bushman

Dr. Thomas Bushur
Dr. LaDon Butler
Dr. David Butler
Dr. David J. Byrnes
Dr. Richard L. Byron
Dr. Brian C. Cadagan
Dr. G. William Caddell
Dr. Robert Caires
Dr. Michael Calhoun
California Chiropractic
    Foundation
Dr. George A. Camacho
Dr. Darren J. Camden
Dr. Michael Camerer
Dr. Geoffrey E. Cameron
Dr. Cary F. Camp
Dr. James W. Campbell
Canadian Memorial
    Chiropractic College
Dr. Catherine E. Canty
Dr. Joseph Canu
Dr. Mark Capodanno
Dr. Michael Capogna
Dr. Nancy Cappiello
Dr. Paul F. Carey
Dr. Kent G. Carlomagno
Dr. Carol J. Carmien
Dr. Marilyn I. Carmona
Dr. Richard E. Carnival
Dr. Stephen A. Carpenter
Dr. Louis S. Carr
Dr. Mark Carrick
Dr. Lori E. Carrillo
Dr. Anthony J. Carrino
Dr. Sam Caruso
Dr. Rodney W. Casada
Dr. J. Stanley Casebere
Dr. James E. Casper
Dr. Edward J. Casper
Dr. James W. Cassillo
Dr. Paul L. Caton
Dr. Doug Cavanaugh
Dr. Cynthia Ceier
Dr. Ernest R. Centofanti
Dr. Marcia R. Cerutty
Dr. Mario Cervino
Dr. Robert P. Chambers
Dr. Mitchell Chambers
Dr. Henry H.K. Chan
Dr. Geoffrey Chan
Dr. Susan Chan
Dr. Michael D. Chance
Dr. David Chapman-Smith
Dr. Gregory B. Chappell
Dr. Gordon W. Charboneau
Dr. Joel N. Charles
Dr. Keith H. Charlton

## BOOK PURCHASE
### (Cont.)

Dr. Kevin L. Cheely
Dr. Chung Hugh Chen
Dr. Roger Chevrefils
Dr. Wai K. Chiang
Dr. Rene J. Chicoine
Dr. Sandra K. Chilson
Dr. Michael Chimes
Dr. Daniel J. Chiodo
Kim Chris
Dr. Soren Christiansen
Dr. Rex D. Christy
Dr. L. John Cianciolo
Dr. Arnold E. Cianciulli
Dr. Frank Cicirello
Dr. John E. Cintineo
Dr. Betty J. Ciuchta
Dr. Michael D. Clancey
Dr. Lewis Clark
Dr. Dale E. Clark
Dr. Lois M. Clark
Dr. Robert W. Clark
Dr. Kathleen Clarkin
Dr. Karl D. Clarkson
Dr. Carol Claus
Dr. Lawrence Clayman
Dr. Ashley E. Cleveland
Dr. Lance E. Cleveland
Cleveland Chiropractic
    College Bookstore,
    Kansas City
Cleveland Chiropractic
    College Bookstore,
    Los Angeles
Dr. Carl S. Cleveland, III
Dr. Carl S. Cleveland, Jr
Dr. Cary J. Clifford
Dr. Hugh W. Cline, Jr.
Dr. Wayne G. Clough
Dr. Gerard W. Clum
Dr. Michael Coady
Dr. David J. Coates
Dr. Cheryl Coates
Dr. Jeffrey S. Cobbs
Dr. Mark Cobleigh
Dr. George R. Coder
Stephanie Codoling
Dr. Michael Cody
Dr. Art Coffman
Dr. Chris Coffman
Dr. Deborah A. Cognata
Dr. Jeffrey H. Cohen
Dr. Lori R. Cohen
Dr. Gary Cohen
Dr. Jean Cohen
Dr. Dale I. Cohen

Dr. Michael J. Cohen
Dr. Howard Cohn
Dr. Patricia E. Coker
Dr. Larry W. Cole
Dr. James T. Cole
Dr. Caren Cole
Dr. Don E. Cole
Dr. Rebekah Collins
Dr. Michael L. Collins
Dr. Lindsay R. Collins
Dr. Roger E. Combs
Dr. Chad Combs
Dr. Lynn R. Conant
Dr. Theodore Conger
Dr. Lynn Connaughty
Dr. Christopher S.
    Connaughty
Dr. Thomas M. Connelly
Dr. Mary M. Connors
Dr. Donald S. Cook
Dr. William E. Copes
Dr. Michael C. Copland-
    Griffiths
Dr. Daniel E. Cordry
Dr. Louis Corleto
Dr. Philip R. Corthier
Dr. Ann Marie Coryell
Dr. Matthew D. Costantino
Dr. Terry Coulits
Dr. Victoria Couluris
Dr. Adrian Couzner
Dr. Robert Cowin
Dr. Douglas B. Cox
Dr. Donald J. Cox
Dr. Curtis N. Cox
Dr. W. Alex Cox
Dr. Robert E. Cox, Jr.
Dr. Victor G. Coxon
Dr. Dennis M. Cozzocrea
Dr. Bruce Crabtree
Dr. Rochard H. Craft
Dr. LonnieCrafton
Dr. Arthur E. Crago
Dr. Michael A. Craven
Dr. Cheryl Crawford
Dr. Dean Crawford
Mr. Michael Crawford
Dr. Arthur C. Croft
Dr. Paul F. Cronk
Dr. Fred B. Crownover
Dr. Kenneth Csillag
Dr. Harold R. Culver
Dr. Rodney L. Cummings
Dr. William E. Cunico
Dr. J. David Currie
Dr. Douglas Curzan
Dr. Stanley M. Cusak

Dr. Terry R. Custer
Dr. Maurice J. Cyr
Dr. Joseph C. D'Angiolillo
Dr. Pierre Claes
    D'Erckenteel
Dr. Rodolfo A. Dabalos
Dr. John J. Daccardi
Dr. Jens Dahl
Dr. Michael R. Dahms
Dr. William H. Dallas
Dr. John Daniels
Dr. Dennis K. Dannefer
Dr. Randy J. David
Dr. Eugene N. Davidson
Dr. Michael S. Davidson
Dr. Mark A. Davini
Dr. Mark A. Davis
Shawn Davis
Dr. Ernest L. Davis
Dr. Connie F. Davis
Dr. Alan J. Davis
Dr. Alfred Davis, Jr
Dr. Laura Dawson
Dr. Lauren D. Dayya
Dr. Madeline De Cesare
Dr. George De Koekkoek
Dr. Gary J. De Wet
Dr. O. Nelson DeCamp, Jr.
Dr. Dennis J. DeLoretta
Dr. Charles L. DeMarco
Dr. Ronald S. DeMars
Dr. William L. DeMoss
Dr. Nipur DeSai
Dr. Anthony S. DeSano
Dr. Sheldon C. Deal
Dr. Donald H. Dearth
Dr. Mark W. Decesare
Dr. Brett P. Decesare
Dr. Mark Deitch
Dr. Ian M. Deitch
Dr. Adam J. Del Torto, Jr.
Dr. Philippe H. Delit
Dr. Phyllis M. Della-Croce
Dr. Mark L. Delmonte
Dr. James Denito
Dr. Gary Dennis
Dr. Weldon L. Derifield
Dr. Peter J. Derig
Dr. Jacinthe Desmarais
Dr. Diane M. Desmond
Dr. Lavern F. Desplinter
Dr. Brent Detelich
Dr. James C. Detelich
Dr. Kathleen Deutsch
Dr. Frederick Deutsch
Dr. Joel A. Deutscher
Dr. Jeffrey S. Devine

Dr. Anders Devold
Dr. Gary DiBenedetto
Dr. Jack DiBenedetto
Dr. Sonya J. DiDomenico
Dr. Philip M. DiPasquale
Dr. Luigi DiRubba
Dr. Deborah L. Diaz
Dr. Andrew Dibley
Dr. Michael J. Dibley
Dr. Paul W. Dickerson
Dr. Rollie Dickinson
Dr. Christopher Diem
Dr. Allen L. Diercks
Dr. Richard J. Dietzen
Dr. Rick Digregorio
Dr. Veronica Dillion
Dr. Colin R. Dingle
Dr. Howard Dinner
Dr. Linda S. Dirlam
Dr. Kurt Doherty
Dr. Leslie A. Dolezal
Dr. David J. Dolinar
Dr. Robert A. Dominguez
Dr. Joseph H. Donahue
Dr. Jeffrey L. Donay
Dr. Beth Donohue
Dr. Danuek A. Dopps
Dr. Frederick P. Dopps
Dr. John D. Doriss
Dr. Michael Dority
Dr. Brad A. Double
Dr. Phillip Doudua
Dr. William J. Doyle
Dr. Sokratis Dragonas
Dr. Anthony J. Dragosh
Dr. Robert G. Dreyer
Dr. Daniel R. Driscoll
Dr. Douglas L. Drobbin
Shannon DuBois
Dr. George F. Dubbs
Dr. Robert E. Dubro
Dr. Gregory A. Dudek
Dr. Richard Duenas
Dr. Paull F. Duffy
Dr. Mary Ann Duffy
Dr. Robin Dugmore
Dr. Glenda F. Dukes
Dr. Christina M. Dumbadse
Dr. Robert W. Duncalf
Dr. Judy Duncalf
Dr. Jim Duncan
Dr. Ronald C. Duncan
Dr. Thomas A. Dunlap
Dr. Marcus Dunn
Dr. Cathy Dunn
Dr. Fawn Dunphy
Dr. Willa D. Duree

Dr. Matthew Durham
Dr. Sherry L. Durrett
Dr. Jeffrey Durski
Dynaspine, Inc.
Dr. Carol Dyson-Busse
Dr. Don F. Eberhardt
Dr. William L. Eblen
Dr. Ronald W. Eccles
Stephen Eckstone, PhD.
Dr. Douglas Edwards
Dr. James D. Edwards
Dr. Richard P. Edwards
Dr. Gary F. Edwards
Dr. David Eggers
Dr. David V. Eggers
Dr. Kevin D. Eichelberger
Dr. Eric Eiselt
Dr. Michael Eklund
Dr. Richard A. Elbert
Dr. Leigh Elceser
Dr. Donald P. Eldridge
Dr. Ramon E. Eldridge
Dr. Juan Elizalde-Caller
Dr. Frederick Elkins
Dr. Ralph G. Ellenberger
Dr. Blaine V. Ellingson
Dr. Wes Elliott
Dr. Shelby M. Elliott
Dr. Horace C. Elliott
Dr. Elizabeth M. Elliott
Dr. David S. Ellis
Dr. E. Paul Emery
Dr. Mitsumasa Endo
Dr. Steven W. Engen
Dr. Jerry R. England
Dr. Donald R. England
Dr. David W. Engstrom
Dr. Carl R. Enlow
Dr. Jeffry J. Ensign
Dr. Jeri S. Epstein
Dr. Vincent J. Erario, Jr.
Dr. Wanda J. Erdman
Dr. Nils Erichsen
Dr. Norris A. Erickson
Dr. Jennifer Eriksen
Dr. William C. Eriksen
Dr. Charles L. Ertel
Dr. David P. Esarco
Dr. John A. Esarco
Dr. Will Evans
Dr. Kathy Evans
Dr. Charles M. Evans
Dr. Dwayne Evans
Dr. Charles E. Everett, Sr.
Dr. Kais Faddah
Dr. Daniel J. Fahnestock
Dr. Timothy A. Failing

## BOOK PURCHASE
(Cont.)

Dr. Catherine M. Falk
Dr. Victor H. Fantasia
Dr. Ronald J. Farabaugh
Dr. Aaron Farber
Dr. Frank S. Farkas
Dr. Roger C. Farmer
Dr. Richard Farmer
Dr. Stanley J. Farr
Dr. Bradley G. Farr
Dr. Gary L. Farr
Dr. Virginia A. Fatato
Dr. Brenda Faulkner
Dr. James R. Fausey
Dr. Richard R. Fay
Dr. Jeffrey S. Fedorko
Dr. Patricia A. Felder
Dr. Elinor F. Feldman
Dr. Marc H. Feldman
Dr. Leonard Feldman
Dr. Carl E. Feltz
Dr. Jeffery Ferdorko
Dr. Edmond E. Ferguson
Dr. Dennis Ferguson
Dr. Jon J. Ferguson
Dr. Peter D. Ferguson
Dr. Steven L. Fetzer
Dr. Ralph M. Filson
Dr. Richard Finder
Dr. Raymond E. Finegan
Dr. Ronald L. Firestone
Dr. Rebecca S. Fischer
Dr. Edward Fisher
Dr. Robert L. Fiss
Dr. Henry J. Fitch
Dr. Dennis Fitterer
Dr. Don E. Fitz-Ritson
Dr. Anne Fitzpatrick
Dr. Sharla Wall Flack
Dr. Cheryl L. Flatin
Dr. Lois A. Flemming
Dr. Gregory A. Flerchinger
Dr. Susan L. Fleuchaus
Dr. Jerald L. Flinn
Dr. John G. Florendo
Dr. Troy E. Fluent
Dr. John J. Flynn
Dr. J. Michael Flynn
Gene Flynn
Dr. Kevin Fogarty
Dr. Cynthia A. Follen
Folletts Chiropractic
  Bookstore
Dr. Jerome E. Fonke
Fonteyn Medical Books
Dr. G.P. Foran

Dr. Thomas E. Forbach
Dr. Darrell E. Fore
Dr. Mario Forieri
Dr. Judy A. Forrester
Dr. Charles Foster
Dr. David Foti
Dr. Mark P. Foullong
Dr. David B. Fox
Dr. Faye Fox
Dr. Kent C. Fox
Dr. Dale L. Frack
  Franz Pietzcker Bookstore
Dr. Margaret Frazier
Dr. Timothy J. Free
Dr. Terry K. Freitag
Dr. Judith H. Frey
Dr. Lawrence E. Frieder
Dr. Louise A. Froehlich-
  Ritchie
Dr. Mark Fronczak
Dr. Howard Frye
Dr. Mechelle Frye-Hanna
Dr. Mario Fucinari
Dr. Deborah A. Fudge
Dr. Paul F. Fulk, Sr.
Dr. Lorna P. Fuller
Dr. Kenneth Fuller
Dr. Garry T. Fuller
Dr. Karon L. Fuller
Dr. John Funnell
Dr. Troels L. Gaarde
Dr. Glenn S. Gabai
Dr. John D. Gaffney
Dr. Melanie S. Gale
Dr. Diana C. Galish-Frasier
Dr. Anne M. Gallagher
Dr. Christian J. Gallastegui
Dr. Kathleen M. Galligan
Dr. Edward J. Galvin, Jr.
Dr. Ron Galy
Dr. Angela Gambale
Dr. Matthew Gamber
Dr. Samuel M. Gamber
Dr. Beatrice Gamble
Dr. Elva M. Gamino
Dr. Craig Gangwish
Dr. Robert Garfinkel
Dr. William G. Garl
Dr. William L. Garmett
Dr. Stephen Garnett
Dr. Kim Garnham
Dr. James P. Garrett
Dr. Phillip C. Gawthrop
Dr. Patricia G. Gayman
Dr. Jeffrey P. Gehlsen
Dr. Betty J. Gelardi
Dr. Thomas A. Gelardi

Dr. Joyce A. Gelles
Dr. Marc Gemerman
Dr. Gary L. Gendron
Dr. Marianne Gengenbach
Dr. Salvatore Gennero, Jr.
Dr. Mark Gentile
Dr. Judith D. Genung
Dr. Michele K. Gerard
Dr. John H. Gerath
Dr. Lincoln German
Dr. Lawrence M. Gerstein
Georgann Gervasi
Dr. Robert J. Gevers
Dr. Edwin C. Gibbs
Dr. Richard Giguere
Dr. Craig E. Gilbaugh
Dr. Harold K. Gilbertson, Sr.
Dr. David P. Gilkey
Dr. Richard Gilmore
Dr. Paul C. Gilmore
Dr. Vicki S. Gilthvedt
Dr. Harley D. Gilthvedt
Dr. Ralph P. Gingerich
Dr. Dave A. Ginsberg
Dr. Jeffrey Gischia
Dr. Edward A. Giuntini
Dr. R. Tyler Given
Dr. Herman H. Glass, II
Dr. Norman J. Gloekler
Dr. Joseph T. Goben
Dr. Kevin L. Goben
Dr. Jon J. Godfrey, Sr.
Dr. Nelson T. Goff
Dr. Gregory A. Goffe
Dr. Joel Goldwasser
Dr. C.W. Gonstead
Dr. Pedro J. Gonzalez-Garcia
Dr. George Goodheart
Dr. Janine Goodheart
Dr. Roger Goodheart
Dr. Robert J. Goodman
Dr. George A. Goodman
Dr. Kenneth J. Goodman
Dr. G. Bevan Goodreid
Dr. Heidi B. Goodwin-
  Ensign
Dr. Roger Gosselin
Dr. Masahiro Goto
Dr. Cameron P. Grade
Dr. Chester D. Graham
Dr. Kenneth S. Graham
Dr. John Graham
Dr. Learie G. Graham
Dr. Robert J. Graham
Dr. Petter Gran
Dr. Kevin K. Granger
Dr. Ron H. Grant

Dr. Bradley R. Grant
Dr. Billy D. Grant
Dr. Ian A. Grassam
Dr. Alvin C. Graun
Dr. James A. Gray
Dr. Robert Graykowski
Dr. Russell Grazier
Dr. Vincent Greco
Dr. Richard F. Green
Green Line Medical Books
Dr. Doug Greenspan
Dr. Jan S. Greenstein
Dr. Philip Greenwood
Dr. R. James Gregg
Dr. Robert A. Gregory
Dr. Lyle W. Grenz
Dr. Ronald J. Gretz
Dr. Adrian S. Grice
Dr. Lynn E. Griffin
Dr. Stephen S. Grim
Dr. Robert J. Grinsell
Dr. James A. Griswold
Dr. James P. Groene
Dr. John F. Grone
Dr. Arndt J. Gronstvedt
Dr. Curtis A. Gross
Dr. FarrellGrossman
Dr. Jack Groves
Dr. Michael R. Gruich
Dr. John P. Grumish
Dr. Ira J. Grusback
Dr. Charles T. Guarisco
Dr. John F. Guerriere
Dr. Jack L. Guilliams
Dr. Troy Gustafson
Dr. Robert H. Guzek
Dr. Bruce H. Hagen
Dr. Hege Hagen
Dr. David L. Hagen
Donald Halcrow
Dr. Samuel S. Haley
Dr. Rory Hall
Dr. Gary W. Hall
Dr. Finn M. Halle
Dr. Davin L. Halpern
Dr. Leon W. Halsted
Dr. Mohsen Hamadanchi
Dr. Hossein Hamadanchi
Dr. Rehana Hamid
Dr. Pernille Eich Hammer
Dr. Steven B. Hammerstrom
Dr. Roger L. Hammerstrom
Dr. Ralph C. Hammett
Dr. Randall J. Hammett
Dr. Michael W. Hanczaryk
Dr. John C. Hanna
Dr. Steve B. Hansen

Dr. Ben F. Hanssen
Dr. Paul J. Harbosky
Dr. Gary E. Harcourt
Dr. Randolph C. Harding
Dr. Dean E. Harniss
Dr. Cynthia Harrington
Dr. Kenneth H.C. Harris
Dr. Eddie T. Harris
Dr. William M. Harris
Dr. Dean J. Harrison
Dr. Marlin F. Harrison
Dr. Kenneth R. Harrison
Dr. Allen J. Harrison
Dr. Donald Harrison
Dr. Patrick L. Hart
Dr. Michael Hart
Dr. Richard L. Hartman
Dr. Michael A. Hartman
Dr. Randall L. Hartman, Sr.
Dr. Richard R. Hasenmeier
Dr. D. Gordon Hasick
Dr. Jeffrey C. Hatfield
Dr. Are Haus
Dr. Deborah Havens
Dr. Gregory Hawthorne
Dr. Melanie J. Hawthorne
Dr. Yuka Hayashida
Dr. William R. Heath
Dr. George Heathcote
Dr. Brian Heaton
Dr. Lindsey Heaton
Dr. Joel Heer
Dr. Glen A. Heese
Dr. J. Peter Heffernan
Dr. Lawrence E. Heffron
Dr. William A. Heffron
Dr. Kurt Hegetschweiler
Dr. Andrew J. Heib
Dr. Carl Heigl
Dr. Sandi Heim
Dr. Roger D. Heimensen
Dr. Laverne R. Heine
Dr. Charles H. Hellem
Chad C. Henderson
Dr. Raymond W. Henderson
Dr. Ivan T. Hendren
Dr. David Hendrey
Dr. Bradley R. Hennen
Dr. Scott Henrichs
Dr. Niels Henriksen
Dr. Bruce D. Hermann
Dr. Steven T. Hernandez
Dr. Donald L. Herndon
Rudy Herrera
Dr. W. Curtis Herwig
Dr. Dennis Heskett
Dr. Frederick R. Hess

## BOOK PURCHASE (Cont.)

Dr. Elmer H. Hester
Dr. Gunnar I. Hetland
Dr. Paul R. Hetrick
Dr. Steven C. Hickey
Dr. Frank G. Hideg, Jr.
Dr. Greg P. Hilger
Dr. Sharon S. Hill
Dr. Russell E.W. Hill
Dr. Jeffrey L. Hill
Dr. Daniel Hill
Dr. John W. Hill
Dr. Daniel P. Hillis
Dr. Margery Hinebaugh
Dr. Michael D. Hinkens
Dr. Gerard C. Hinley
Dr. James A. Hinsch
Dr. Paul M. Hinton
Dr. Judith A. Hinwood
Dr. John A. Hinwood
Dr. Yuka Hirose
Dr. Eugene L. Hirscg
Dr. Larry D. Hirschy
Dr. Donald W. Hirsh
Dr. Stephen M. Hoard
Dr. Christina Hoard
Dr. Henrik Hoejgaard
Dr. Stuart E. Hoffman
Dr. Frank A. Hoffman
Dr. Ellen M. Hoffman
Dr. Robert Hoffman
Dr. John A. Hofmann
Dr. Wende K. Hofmann
Dr. Craig C. Hollowell
Dr. Claire M. Holman
Dr. William F. Holmberg
Dr. Arthur W. Holmes
Dr. David P. Holtrop
Dr. Mark C. Holtschlag
Dr. G. Todd Holubitsky
Dr. Volkhart Homann
Dr. Robert J. Homonai
Dr. John Homza
Dr. Hiroe Honda
Dr. Richard W. Hooke
Dr. Paul R. Hoover
Daniel L. Hoover
Dr. Thomas Horn
Dr. Philip B. Horner
Dr. John Horner
Dr. Dominique Hort
Dr. Mark W. Houk
Dr. Brian House
Dr. Lucinda J. Hovi
Dr. G. Matt Howard III
Dr. Jonathan M. Howat

Dr. Douglas K. Howell
Karen Hsu
Dr. Diana J. Hudgins
Dr. Kreg D. Huffer
Dr. David B. Huffman
Dr. P. Reginald Hug
Dr. Bronwyn Hughes
Dr. Harold T. Hughes
Dr. Rita A. Hughes
Dr. John C. Hui
Dr. William J. Huizenga
Dr. Hobart H. Hull
Dr. Roger D. Hulsebus
Dr. Michael J. Hulsebus
Dr. Robert L. Hulsebus
Dr. James P. Hulsebus
Dr. Dale K. Hultgren
Dr. Durie D. Humber
Dr. Stuart Humberg
Dr. Harry E. Hunt
Dr. Philip A. Hurd
Dr. Robert Hurst
Dr. Hugh C. Hurst
Dr. Bob Hurst
Dr. Randall Hurt
Dr. Roger D. Hurt
Dr. Richard E. Husle
Dr. Ian M. Hutchinson
Dr. Michele Hutchinson-Nutter
Dr. Floyd P. Huxford
Dr. Christine A. Hyman
Dr. Robin C. Hyman
Dr. Grant CIannelli
Dr. AkibaIbura
Dr. Andrew K. Iggo
Dr. MotoharuIkeda
Dr. Keith AInnes
Dr. Tatsuya Inoue
Dr. Virginia S. Irby
Dr. Richard A. Irby
Dr. Trevor V. Ireland
Dr. Brett G. Ireland
Dr. Geoffrey Irvine
Dr. Joseph G. Irwin
Dr. Tsuneo Ito
Dr. Christopher L. Ivers
Dr. Joyce Ivy-Price
Dr. Peter Jacelone
Dr. David A. Jackson
Dr. Lisa A. Jackson
Dr. Anita K. Jackson
Dr. Kevin Jackson
Dr. Gary A. Jacob
Dr. Carla S. Jacobs
Dr. Larry M. Jacobs
Dr. Bent Jacobsen

Dr. Barbara Jacobsen
Dr. William W. Jacobson
Dr. Dirk Jacobsz
Dr. Renee Jacquette
Dr. Spence Jahner
Dr. Patricia Jamison
Dr. Roya Jamshidi
Dr. Kirby C. Janke
Dr. Jack Janulis
Dr. Barbara Jeffery
Dr. Alfred H. Jenness
Dr. Dixie A. Jepson
Dr. Andrew S. Jeter
Dr. Dermot Jinks
Dr. Carl H. Johannessen
Dr. Espen Johannessen
Dr. Diane L. Johnson
Dr. Lance Johnson
Dr. David W. Johnson
Dr. John M. Johnson
Dr. Lars Johnson
Dr. Robert Johnson
Dr. John P. Johnson
Dr. Cindy Johnson
Dr. Karl R. Johnson
Dr. John M. Johnsrud
Dr. Jean Paul Jolivet
Dr. Daniel M. Jones
Dr. Michael B. Jones
Dr. Patsy R. Jones
Dr. Daniel D. Jones
Dr. Shawn R. Jones
Dr. Rochelle M. Jones
Dr. Timothy S. Joplin
Dr. John S. Jordan
Dr. Karl M. Jordan
Dr. D. Joseph
Dr. Gregory L. Judd
Dr. Brian D. Justice
Dr. Rick L. Justice
Dr. Palmera E. Kabana
Dr. Jerry E. Kadolph
Dr. Sinja Kahkonen
Dr. Terry L. Kahn
Dr. Kenton D. Kainz
Dr. Michiko Kajita
Dr. Melvin H. Kallsen
Dr. Albert R. Kalter
Dr. Joseph R. Kanan
Dr. Ben Kaplan
Dr. Michael F. Kapraun
Erik Karjalainen
Dr. Roger Kasperbauer
Dr. Udo Kastner
Dr. Lonnie G. Katro
Dr. LLoyd C. Katz
Dr. Steven L. Katz

Dr. Nitha M. Kauffold-White
Dr. Yozo Kawanishi
Dr. Christine Keidel-DiBenedetto
Dr. Gregory L. Keilman
Dr. John P. Keils
Dr. Ronald G. Keleman
Dr. Rickey D. Keller
Dr. Carl Keller
Dr. Charles J. Keller
Dr. Richard J. Kelly
Dr. James Randall Kelly
Dr. Mark S. Kemenosh
Dr. Rocky Kemp
Dr. Graham J. Kenyon
Dr. Keith L. Kermeen
Dr. Robert Kessinger
Dr. Anfinn Kilvaer
Dr. Stephen W. Kimball
Dr. Mildred L. Kimbrough
Dr. Mark S. Kimes
Dr. Willie W. Kindred
Dr. William D. King
Dr. Wallace E. King
Dr. Leon King
Scott Kirchner
Dr. Christopher J. Klaes
Dr. Gary W. Klaudt
Dr. Darrel D. Klemp
Dr. Joel R. Kleven
Dr. Mark S. Klezmer
Dr. Gary P. Kliebenstein
Dr. Richard M. Klingert
Dr. Robert F. Klinginsmith
Dr. Linda Klinginsmith-Tilford
Dr. John F. Klug
Dr. James A. Klug
Dr. Matthew E. Klumpp
Dr. Ulla Kjaer Knudsen
Dr. Nobuaki Kobayashi
Dr. Casimer Kobylinski, Jr.
Dr. Lynne Koch
Dr. Craig C. Koehler
Dr. James R. Koenen
Dr. Richard P. Koenen
Dr. Jeane R. Koenen
Dr. James R. Koenen
Dr. Jack R. Koenen
Dr. Louis I. Koff
Dr. Jean F. Koffel
Dr. Frank Kohlbeck
Dr. Alain M. Kolt
Dr. Gerald D. Kortmeyer
Dr. James Koshick
Dr. Thomas Kosmyna

Dr. William C. Kragen
Dr. Warren Kragt
Dr. Edwin J. Kragt
Dr. John B. Kragt
Dr. Kim W. Krantz
Dr. Andrew H. Krantz
Dr. Steven J. Kraus
Dr. Lori Krauss
Dr. James C. Kreger
Dr. T. Kreusch
Dr. William L. Krieger
Dr. Kay A. Kristensen
Dr. Peter Kristiansen
Dr. Brian L. Kroes
Dr. John P. Krueger
Ingrid Kruse
Dr. Michael J. Kruse
Dr. Paul Krynen
Dr. Suzan Kudick
Dr. Denise C. Kufeldt
Dr. Kathryn Ann Kulba
Dr. Alan H. Kunkel
Dr. Kenneth P. Kurba
Dr. Muffie G. Kurthy
Dr. Randall Kurtz
Dr. Hing L. Kwan
Dr. Edward R. Kwasniewski
Dr. Edmund Kwong
Dr. Arthur A. La Bella
Dr. Richard J. T. LaBarbera
Dr. Joseph A. LaBarbera
Dr. Frank J. Labate
Dr. Norbert J. Labine
Dr. Jeff Labinger
Dr. Jean Lachance
Dr. Benoit Lagace
Dr. Patrick A. Lalama
Dr. Gail J. Lamirande
Dr. France Lamothe
Dr. Patrick Landau
Dr. Gregory A. Landau
Dr. Paul Lang
Dr. G. Edward Langdon
Dr. James W. Langford
Dr. Stanmore G. Langford III
Dr. Cheryl Langley
Dr. Jennifer Langworthy
Dr. Charles Lantz
Dr. Robert A. Lapuck
Dr. Stewart L. Larbell
Dr. Karen M. Larsen
Dr. Stacy Larson
Dr. Sherri L. Lashomb
Dr. Gary L. Latimer
Dr. Lyle L. Lauritsen
Dr. Elizabeth Lavin
Dr. Herbert S. Law

Dr. Kenneth H. Law-Davis
Dr. Andrew D. Lawrence
Dr. Dana Lawrence
Dr. Sheila K. Laws
Dr. Ronald S. Laws
Dr. Bobby G. Lawson
Dr. Gordon E. Lawson
Dr. John C. Lawyer
Dr. Ellen Lazar
Dr. Michelle Lazerow
Dr. Lynn R. LeBel
Dr. Henri L. LeBel
Dr. Daniel LeBell
Dr. Carol LeBlanc
Dr. Russell LeBlanc
Dr. David G. Leach
Dr. Charlotte Leahy
Dr. George Lechman
Dr. Paula R. Lee
Dr. Chun Lee
Dr. James T. Lefebvre
Dr. Gerald Legault
Dr. Jacqueline Legault
Dr. Karen L. Lehman
Dr. James J. Lehman
Dr. Michelle Lehotay
Dr. Sam Leibowitz
Dr. Kevin Lenin
Dr. Arthur Lensgraf
Dr. Leif Lensgraf
Dr. Eric L. Lensgraf
Dr. Stephanie A. Leonard
Dr. Neal Lepovetsky
Dr. Ben S. Lerner
Dr. Eric S. Lerner
Dr. Robert Lerner
Dr. Claude Lessard
Dr. Guylaine Lessard
Dr. Josee Lessard-Homza
Dr. Marc Leuenberger
Dr. Constante Levesque
Dr. Ellen Lewis
Dr. Kasey Lewis
Dr. Ronald Ley
Dr. Kim M. Licausi
Dr. Alan J. Lichter
Life College of Chiropractic
Dr. Kenneth L. Lim
Dr. Jorn S. Lindbach
Dr. Teresa H. Litchfield
Dr. Thomas M. Little
Dr. Noel G. Lloyd
Dr. John D. Locknenour
Dr. James M. Loftus
Dr. Daniel S. Loftus

Logan College of
  Chiropractic
Dr. Sheila E. Lois
Dr. Charles L. Long
Dr. Edward M. Long
Dr. Timothy B. Long
Dr. Rick B. Longie
Longus Book Imports
Dr. Brian K. Loranger
Dr. Anna Loranger
Dr. Lisa B. Loranger
Dr. Tony M. Lorber
Dr. Lance Lorfeld
Los Angeles Chiropractic
  College
Dr. Jeffrey C. Lotzer
Dr. Kevin J. Loughlin
Dr. Timothy W. Love
Dr. Roy M. Love
Dr. Larry J. Lovejoy
Dr. Lisa Lovett
Dr. Peter W. Lovgren
Dr. Kevin D. Lowey
Dr. Allan Lowman
Dr. Kenneth M. Lowrey
Dr. Jack A. Lube
Dr. George J. Lubertazzo
Dr. Mark E. Luce
Dr. Vincent P. Lucido
Dr. Kenneth L. Luedtke
Dr. Scott Lund
Dr. Iben Lundbye-
  Kristiansen
Dr. Chad Lundstrom
Dr. Judith R. Luongo
Dr. Morris Lutes
Dr. Richard Lynch
Dr. R. Lee MacAllister
Dr. Russell MacDonald
Dr. Raymond J. MacDonald
Dr. Michael MacLeod
Dr. Scott B. Macaulay
Dr. Jack Macrone
Dr. Dawn M. Maddalone
Dr. Mary E. Madden
Dr. Michael D. Maddox
Dr. Glen D. Madsen
Dr. Tim Maguire
Dr. John P. Maher
Dr. Carol Mahoney
Dr. Janet E. Major
Dr. Jeffrey Majors
Dr. Gregory S. Malakoff
Dr. James J. Malavolti
Dr. Kerri Maliszewski-
  Barton
Dr. John P. Maltese

Dr. James E. Manard
Dr. Daniel J. Mancini
Dr. Carol M. Mancini
Dr. Steven Mandell
Dr. Bill Manfull
Dr. Donna Mannello
Dr. Jerry A. Mantonya
Dr. Jack D. Manuele
Dr. Jack A. Manzella
Dr. Vincent L. Maples
Dr. Laurent Maratrat
Dr. Sharon K. March
Dr. Nalyn R. Marcus
Dr. John M. Markey
Dr. Harvey J. Markovitz
Dr. Glenn Marks
Dr. Rick Markson
Dr. Lawrence T. Markson
Dr. Mike Marshall
Dr. John L. Marth
Dr. Ernesto Marticorena
Dr. Robert C. Martin
Dr. Peter A. Martin
Dr. Avery H. Martin
Dr. Petrus Martin
Dr. Piet Martin
Dr. Michael J. Martin
Dr. Mary K. Martin
Dr. Susan M. Martin
Dr. Michael A. Martinez
Dr. Margaret Martinez
Dr. Joseph J. Martini
Dr. Rhonda Marty
Dr. E.G. Marty, Jr.
Dr. Naoki Maruyama
Dr. Charles S. Masarsky
Dr. Jim L. Mask
Dr. Jack S. Mask
Dr. Trevor J. Maskell
Dr. Steven Massey
Dr. Ronald Masters
Dr. Blair B. Masters
Dr. Ronald O. Masters II
Dr. Frank P. Mathias
Dr. Andrew L. Mathias
Dr. Irvin T. Mathias
Dr. Loujan Matin
Dr. Gerald R. Mattia
Dr. Ed Maurer
Dr. Debra L. May
Dr. Maxine C. Mayreis
Dr. Clifton Mays
Dr. Jerome F. McAndrews
Dr. Randy W. McCall
Dr. Roy J. McCallum
Dr. James R. McCanse
Dr. Heather M. McClary

Dr. James D. McClary
Dr. Daniel McClellan
Dr. George B. McClelland, Jr.
Dr. James T. McCoskey
Dr. Donald E. McCune
Dr. William P. McDonald
Dr. Jeanne S. McDowall
Dr. Donald A. McDowall
Dr. Joseph T. McEachron
Dr. Gregory C. McFadzean
Dr. Edward J. McGinnis
Dr. Eileen McGough
Dr. Timothy G. McGraw
McGraw Hill Bookstore
Dr. Tim J. McKay
Dr. Edward D. McKenzie
Dr. Thomas McLaughlin
Dr. Patricia F. McLean
Dr. Gary R. McLeod
Dr. Campbell A. McLeod
Dr. Curtiss A. McLeod
Dr. Michael T. McLogan
Dr. J. Michael McMahon
Dr. Rick A. McMichael
Dr. Richard A. McMullen
Dr. D. Michael McPeak
Dr. Loren E. McReynolds
Dr. Truman McVay
Dr. Willie Mccray
Dr. Mary P. Medwar
Dr. Steve A. Meeks
Dr. Stacy Meeks
Dr. Ignaas Meersseman
Dr. Jean-Pierre Meersseman
Dr. Bradley J. Meints
Dr. Beth A. Meints
Dr. Douglas L. Meints
Dr. Frank R. Meisel
Dr. David Melendez
Dr. Diane M. Melendrez
Dr. Mark Meleski
Dr. Michael A. Meleski
Dr. Robert S. Mellette
Dr. Timothy E. Meng
Dr. Linda Meola
Dr. Ronald P. Meola
Dr. Maria Mercedes
  Montano
Dr. Christopher J. Mertz
Dr. James E. Messimer
Dr. Tania Messina-Howard
Dr. Anthony M. Metcalfe
Dr. Robert D. Metz
Dr. Michael S. Meyer
Dr. Kenneth J. Meyer
Dr. Robert H. Meyer
Dr. Curtis L. Meyer

Dr. Gilbert Meyronet
Dr. Daniel A. Michalec
Dr. Ronald T. Michalski
Dr. Steven A. Mickelson
Dr. Sam A. Mickey
Dr. Ronald E. Miklebost
Dr. M.L. Milani
Dr. Martin W. Miller
Dr. Donald E. Miller
Dr. Terrence R. Miller
Dr. Constance M. Miller
Dr. Aileen D. Miller
Dr. David A. Miller
Dr. Matthew W. Miller
Dr. Mark D. Miller
Dr. David A. Miller
Dr. Kevin Millet
Dr. Laura Millis
Dr. Gary L. Mills
Dr. Joe C. Minder
Dr. Dennis Minori
Dr. Donald R. Mitchell
Dr. Dennis H. Mizel
Dr. Rupert D. Molloy
Dr. Eduardo J. Montano
Dr. Francisco Montano-
  Benet
Dr. Fransco Montario-
  Pizarro
Dr. Joann Monteiro
Dr. Gabriel Monterrubio
Dr. Denise Szwed
  Montgomery
Dr. James Montgomery
Dr. Patrick Montgomery
Dr. Jim Moore
Dr. John Moore
Dr. Michael J. Moore
Dr. Michael J. Morandini
Dr. Emanuel Morening
Dr. Benjamin P. Morgan
Dr. Bill D. Morgan
Dr. Kenneth Morgan
Dr. Daniel H. Moriarty
Dr. Kazuaki Moriguchi
Dr. Yoshiyuki Morioka
Dr. Arthur G. Mork
Dr. Esther Mork
Dr. John L. Mormile
Dr. Jay L. Morris
Dr. Barrett E. Morrison
Dr. Tim Morrison
Jennifer Morrissey
Dr. Ralph C. Morrow
Dr. Melvin K. Morrow
Dr. Dale E. Mortenson
Dr. Lowry R. Morton

## BOOK PURCHASE
### (Cont.)

Dr. Robert S. Renfro
Dr. Thomas E. Resendez
Dr. Vincent G. Rettay
Dr. Thomas A. Rexroth
Dr. Charlotte Riber
Dr. Scott Ricciardi
Dr. Clark E. Rich
Dr. J.K. Rich
Dr. Gregg Rich
Dr. Paula A. Richard
Dr. Dennis M. Richards
Dr. Philippe Richon
Dr. Christiane Richon
Dr. David A. Ridge
Dr. Paul D. Riegleman
Dr. Michael J. Riemhofer
Dr. David E. Riffel
Dr. Steven C. Riggleman
Dr. Gregory J. Riley
Dr. Imogene Riley
Dr. Cynthia L. Riley
Francine H. Rippy
Dr. Gerard Riquet
Dr. Christa Rivelli
Todd Robert
Dr. Beverly N. Roberts
Dr. William P. Roberts
Dr. Adrian J. Robichaud
Dr. Donald R. Robinson
Dr. G. Lindsay Robson
Dr. Cynthia C. Rocco
Dr. Charles M. Rockwell
Dr. Dennis J. Rodden
Dr. Corey B. Rodnick
Dr. Donna Rodriguez
Dr. Marcio Rodriguez
Dr. Gordon Rody
Dr. Douglas M. Rody
Dr. David J. Roepelle
James Roerig
Dr. Roger R. Roff
Dr. David L. Rogers
Dr. Neil S. Rogers
Dr. Lana Rogerson
Dr. Deanna J. Rogge
Dr. Dale Rohlfing
Dr. Donald L. Rohlfsen
Dr. Peter D. Rohrs
Dr. Dale A. Rollette
Dr. Eleanor L. Rolnick
Dr. Roger M. Romano
Dr. William J. Rooney
Dr. Samuel B. Rose
Dr. Frances M. Rose
Dr. James A. Rosemeyer

Dr. Leo K. Rosenberg
Dr. Scott Rosenthal
Dr. Paul J. Roses
Dr. Gary L. Roshy
Dr. Norman Ross
Dr. Donald D. Ross, Sr.
Dr. Eddy Rosseel
Dr. Sharon C. Roth
Dr. Jefferson A. Roth
Dr. Jason D. Roth
Dr. Therese A. Rotundo
Dr. Patricia S. Rowe
Dr. Richard J. Roy
Dr. Ross S. Royster
Dr. Leslie Rozenhart
Dr. Luis F. Ruano
Dr. Arlen S. Rubin
Dr. Henry M. Rubinstein
Dr. Charles E. Ruckel
Dr. Willard A. Rud
Dr. Brian T. Ruddell
Dr. Kevin Ruddell
Dr. Jon Rumbaugh
Dr. Craig Rummel
Dr. Paul Rumph
Dr. Ronald J. Ruscitti
Dr. Robert A. Rush
Dr. Jack Rushin
Dr. Lawrence R. Russ
Dr. John F. Russo
Dr. Agnes Rutherford
Dr. L.W. Rutherford
Dr. Mary C. Rutkowski
Dr. M. Wanda Rutland
Dr. Danny J. Rutz
Dr. Albert Rymer
Dr. Michael A. Sabia, Sr.
Dr. Chad Sackett
Dr. Douglas C. Sacksteder
Dr. Charles A. Saenz
Dr. Danene M. Saggau
Masai Sahairi
Dr. Raymond Saint
Dr. Hirouki Sako
Dr. Raymond J. Sala
Dr. Susan Salem-Belfer
Dr. Gary D. Sallans
Dr. Thomas Salmon
Dr. Todd Salow
Dr. Sascha Samerski
Dr. R. Barry Sams
Dr. Ronald B. Sanders
Claudia Sandino
Dr. Fredrick R. Santangelo
Dr. James J. Santiago
Joel Santy
Dr. John C. Saponara, Jr

Dr. Scott S. Sardonicus
Dr. Mario Sassi
Dr. Ichiro Sato
Dr. Leonard G. Saulter, Jr
Dr. E. Steven Saunders
Dr. Edward M. Saunders
Dr. Serge Sautre
Dr. Stephen M. Savoie
Dr. Roosevelt L. Savoy
Dr. Souichi Sawada
Dr. Charles E. Sawyer
Dr. John J. Sayers, Jr
Dr. John Sayers, Sr
Dr. Gary W. Schaaf
Dr. David Schacher
Dr. John Schafer
Dr. William G. Schirmer
Dr. Katherine M. Schlaffer
Dr. Joseph S. Schlaffer
Dr. Michael D. Schleicher
Dr. Stephen D. Schlosser
Dr. Frederick Schlueb
Dr. Ronald K. Schmeltzer
Dr. Matthew Schmid
Dr. Jeanne Schmidt
Dr. Wayne E. Schmidt
Dr. Mary Schmidt
Dr. Charles A. Schnier
Dr. Perri Schnier
Dr. Ilene Schofield
Dr. Fred Schofield
Dr. Tracy Schoonover
Dr. Anthony C. Schraedel
Dr. James M. Schroder
Dr. David Schroder
Dr. R.E. Schroeder
Dr. Tim Schroeder
Dr. Ernest Schroeder
Dr. William G. Schroeder
Dr. Rita M. Schroeder
Dr. Mary B. Schultz
Dr. Miriam C. Schultz
Dr. Rodney Schulz
Dr. Larry J. Schumacher
Dr. Tanya Schupbach
Dr. Ben L. Schutte
Dr. Michael Schwager
Dr. Maria Schwarz
Dr. Michael Scimeca
Dr. Steven R. Sciuto
Dr. Guy Scohy
Dr. Katia Scohy
Dr. Gabrielle Scohy-Maes
Dr. Bruce D. Scott
Dr. Charlotte Scott
Dr. Keith G. Scott
Dr. Donald R. Scott

Dr. Robert C. Scott
Dr. Thomas A. Scott
Dr. Catherine Sears
Dr. Steen A. Selander
Dr. Bodil Selboskar
Dr. Kevin L. Self
Dr. Clay O. Selley
Dr. Shelley Sembler
Dr. Bradley G. Semegon
Dr. Lori J. Sender-O'Hara
Dr. Paul Seniw
Dr. Ola Senstad
Dr. Philip M. Serrins
Dr. Scott M. Sessions
Dr. Jamie L. Settimi
Dr. Rodney G. Shaffer
Dr. Mark A. Shaffer
Dr. Nancy Shaler
Dr. Chirag Shan
Dr. Robert Shaner
Dr. Douglas E. Shaw
Dr. Thomas G. Shaw, Jr
Shawn Steel & Associates
Dr. Deborah A. Shea
Dr. Eric A. Shearer
Dr. Jeffrey Shebovsky
Dr. Dean S. Shepherd
Dr. Joseph A. Sheppard
Dr. Shamus Sheridan
Dr. Sean Sheridan
Dr. Alan P. Sherr
Dr. David A. Sherrington
Dr. Sheri A. Sherwood
Dr. Mark Sherwood
Dr. Kurt Sherwood
Dr. Jeannette Sherwood
Dr. Diane Sherwood-Palmer
Dr. Robert Shi
Dr. David A. Shields
Dr. David P. Shields
Dr. Hirohiko Shimazaki
Dr. Michael D. Shinkle
Dr. Randall E. Shipman
Dr. James L. Shoemaker
Dr. Karen Shoemaker
Dr. David A. Shreve
Dr. Mike Shride
Dr. Jack S. Shubin
Dr. Paul D. Shumway
Dr. Anthony P. Siano, Jr
Dr. L.L. Sibley
Dr. Larry Sibley
Dr. Shannon Sichewski
Dr. Thomas J. Sidoti
Dr. Frank J. Siebenaler
Dr. Gerardo O. Siebert
Dr. Daun Sigafoose

Dr. Tina A. Sigafoose
Dr. James M. Sigafoose
Dr. Chris J. Sigafoose
Dr. Selina Sigafoose-Jackson
Dr. Leon Sigler
Dr. Jeanne Sigvardt
Dr. Delores Silverstein
Dr. William V. Simmons
Dr. Vincent Sinclair
Dr. Santokh Sing-Khalsa
Dr. Richard R. Singleton
Dr. Robert J. Sinnott
Dr. Allen P. Sipes
Dr. Vince Siraguso
Dr. Selmar Skibsted
Dr. Wayne D. Skilton
Dr. Albert J. Skocik
Dr. Parrish Skrien
Dr. John A. Slawson
Dr. Herbert C. Sloat
Dr. Dean Sluce
Dr. Robert Small
Dr. Michael C. Smatt
Dr. Lori M. Smatt
Dr. Nancy Smith
Dr. Desmond J. Smith
Dr. Nancy Smith
Dr. Marilyn P. Smith
Dr. James Smith
Dr. Lisa Smith
Dr. William J. Smith
Dr. Scott H. Smith
Dr. Gary L. Smith
Dr. Allene L. Smith
Dr. Joel E. Smooke
Dr. Frank Sniezek
Dr. Rick Snook
Dr. Gregory J. Snow
Dr. James R. Snyder
Dr. Michelle Snyder
Dr. David W. Snyder
Dr. Brian L. Solofsky
Dr. Jerrold Solomon
Dr. Trond Soot
Dr. Halvor Sorbye
Dr. Brian L. Sorell
Dr. Sean Sorell
Dr. Samuel J. Soriero
Dr. Janet R. Sosna
Dr. Michael Spadafino
Dr. Eugene E. Sparlin
Dr. Samuel J. Sparlin
Dr. Kory Spear
Dr. Mark T. Spears
Dr. Shannon L. Speer
Dr. Gary W. Spero
Dr. Deanna M. Spicer

## BOOK PURCHASE
(Cont.)

Dr. Todd E. Spieles
Dr. James A. Spina
  Spinalogic
Dr. William D. Spontak
Dr. Louis Sportelli
Dr. Judson G. Sprandel
Dr. Kenneth D. Spresser
Dr. LaDean L. Spring
Dr. Michael Spurlock
Dr. Lewis G. Squires
Dr. Gerald C. St. John
Dr. Edwin St. John
Dr. Timothy M. Stackis
Dr. Jeff Stackis
Dr. Barry M. Stahl
Dr. Bryce C. Staker
Dr. Alexandra Staker
Standard Process, Inc.
Dr. Barbara Stanfield
Dr. Randall P. Stange
Dr. John K. Stanton
Dr. Felix J. Starker
Dr. George Starkey
Rennie Statler
Dr. Jeanne Staudt
Dr. Robert J. Steck
Dr. Lisa M. Stein
Dr. David Steiner
Dr. Mark A. Steiner
Dr. Zane Sterling
Dr. Robert L. Stevens
Dr. Andrew D. Stevenson
Dr. Susan Steward
Dr. Pamela Stiefvater
Dr. James W. Stinear
Dr. John D. Stites
Dr. Frank G. Stitt
Dr. Ross V. Stokes
Dr. Scott Stoner
Dr. Larry E. Stout
Dr. William Straede
Dr. Virgil V. Strang
Dr. Gary R. Street
Dr. William F. Streiff
Dr. Irwin G. Strickland
Dr. Charles Strickland
Dr. Susan Strobel
Dr. Michael Stroh
Dr. Thomas N. Stroot
Dr. Steven S. Stryker
Dr. Christopher T. Stucchi
Dr. Paul Stuchbery
Dr. Larry J. Stucky
Dr. John L. Stump
Dr. James R. Sullivan

Dr. Louise Sung
Dr. Belen Sunyer
Dr. Claude Supersaxo
Dr. John R. Suyak
Dr. Koichi Suzaki
Dr. Yoshihiro Suzuki
Dr. Val M. Svetich
Dr. Mark Swain
Dr. Brad J. Swanson
Dr. John A. Sweaney
Swedish Library House
Dr. Nicole Sweetman
Dr. Jerome P. Sweiter
Dr. Eugene J. Swella
Dr. Timothy A. Swihart
Dr. Kyle D. Swisher
Dr. David L. Swope
Dr. Paul D. Sykes
Dr. Stephanie Szabo
Dr. Albert D. Szany
Dr. Michael Szapki
Dr. Michael Szapko
Dr. Paull Szwez
Chris Tabick
Dr. Hiroaki Takeyachi
Dr. Nobuyoski Takeyachi
Dr. Kazuyoshi Takeyachi
Dr. Lynne A. Talkowski
Dr. Larry L. Talley
Dr. Steven T. Tamaka
Dr. Edmund F. Tamburrino
Colleen T. Tanaka
Dr. David B. Tanis
Dr. Yoshiki Tanizaki
Dr. Seth T. Tanner
Dr. Jared Tapia
Dr. Laurence Tassell
Dr. Howard L. Taulor
Dr. Anthony Taylor
Dr. Lloyd W. Taylor
Dr. Thomas D. Taylor
Dr. Julia P. Taylor
Dr. Rohan W. Teasdale
Dr. Jefferson K. Teass
Dr. Beth B. Tedesco
Dr. Stephen B. Teeple
Dr. Jan Teitelbaum
Dr. Vanessa A. Teo
Dr. Katsuhiko Terashia
Dr. Thomas E. Terbilcox
Dr. Richard J. Tesoriero
Dr. Stephen Tetzlaff
Dr. John W. Thatcher
Dr. Paige T. Thibodeau
Dr. Mary P. Thiele
Dr. Steven Thiele
Dr. William F. Thimmel

Dr. Mary Jo Thola
Dr. Danita J. Thomas
Dr. Davis L. Thomas
Dr. Otis F. Thomas
Dr. Robert L. Thompsen
Dr. Chris Thompson
Dr. Pam Thompson
Dr. Rex E. Thompson
Dr. Homer R. Thompson
Dr. Erik Thompson
Dr. Gary Thomson
Dr. A.G. Thomson
Dr. Richard E. Thornton
Dr. Carleen A. Thum
Dr. Judith A. Thurber
Dr. James R. Thwaits
Dr. John T. Tierney
Dr. A. Glynn Till
Dr. Patricia M. Tillou
Scott Timpanelli
Dr. Kurt S. Titze
Dr. Wayne H. Todd
Dr. Gordon H. Toftness
Dr. Saori Tonomoto
Dr. Julia A. Tooley
Dr. Hallstein C. Torp
Dr. Joel Torres
Dr. Steven Tougas
Dr. Akihiko Touichi
Dr. Stephen Tranter
Dr. Caroline Triebold
Dr. Michael A. Triglia
Dr. Nancy Trimboli
Dr. Steven R. Troeger
Dr. Jill B. Trull
Dr. Fred L. Trull II
Dr. Yoshitaka Tsuji
Dr. David J. Tucker
Dr. Paul M. Tullio
Dr. Walter Tuminson
Dr. Timothy C. Turino
Dr. Bruce R. Turino
Dr. Linda R. Turley-
  Sweeney
Dr. Clay D. Tuttle
Dr. David S. Tyrell
Dr. Koji Uemura
Dr. Andrew Uhl
Dr. Edward R. Uhler
Dr. Connie M. Unetich
Dr. Joseph F. Unger, Jr
Dr. Michael L. Ungerank
University of Bridgeport
Dr. Allen D. Unruh
Dr. Wally A. Unruh
Dr. G. Douglas Valentine
Dr. Ragna M. Valli

Dr. Gordon R. Valliant
Dr. Jan C. Van Beelen
Dr. C.H. Van Beest
Dr. Rod Van Buskirk
Dr. I. Van Der Venter
Dr. Coralee Van Egmond
Dr. Mervin Van Engen
Dr. Daniel G. Van Gessel
Dr. G. Van Heule
Dr. A. Robert Van Note
Dr. D. Van Rensburg
Dr. Garry K. Van Romer
Dr. Laura Van Wagoner
Dr. Lyndon J. Van Wagoner
Dr. Scott R. Van Wilpe
Dr. Gert T. Van Der Walt
Dr. Lance E. Van Derloo
Dr. Patrick L. Van Quaethem
Dr. James Vana
Dr. Richard L. Vance
Dr. Donald C. Vance
Dr. Jack K. Vandervort
Dr. Steven M. Varney
Dr. George D. Vasbinder
Dr. Bruce S. Vaughan
Dr. Robert M. Vaughn
Dr. George P. Velasco
Dr. Leonard Venezia
Dr. Chad C. Vick
Dr. Luis Vidalon
Dr. Victor M. Vieira
Dr. Nathalie Vijnau-
  Schroeder
Dr. Thomas J. Villeneuve
Dr. Karamjit S. Virk
Dr. Douglas W. Vise
Dr. Steven C. Visentin
Dr. Frederick Vliestra
Dr. Frederick M. Vogel
Dr. Christopher S.
  Vogelmann
Dr. Denise Vuich
Dr. Wallace C. Wade
Dr. Terry Waggoner
Dr. Alvin T. Wahlert
Dr. Timothy S. Wakefield
Dr. Lorelei Wakefield
Dr. Robert W. Wakeland
Dr. Jon Walawitch
Dr. Wayne Walburn
Dr. Michael E. Walker
Dr. R.P. Walker
Dr. John D. Walker
Dr. Dale R. Walker
Dr. Richard Walker
Dr. John R. Wallace
Dr. Susan Walsemann

Dr. Gary Walsemann
Dr. Thomas S. Ward
Dr. Patty B. Ward
Dr. Lois Ward
Dr. Michael W. Ward
Dr. Gary F. Ward
Dr. Jon K. Warnecke
Dr. Theresa M. Warner
Dr. Robert Warner
Dr. Stuart P. Warner
Dr. Timothy Warren
Dr. J. Wray Warren
Dr. Mark J. Warta
Dr. Masakazu Washio
Dr. John D. Waterhouse
Dr. Dawn C. Watkins
Dr. James L. Watkins
Dr. Mary Watkins
Dr. Kimberly D. Watson
Dr. Carol E. Webb
Dr. Dolores G. Webb
Dr. Victoria Webster
Dr. John A. Webster
Dr. Sharon J. Weicman
Dr. Scott T. Weinel
Dr. Mindy A. Weingarten
Dr. Ralph L. Weinhold
Dr. Chip Weisel II
Dr. Bradley J. Weiss
Dr. Robert Welborn
Dr. Ronald J. Wellikoff
Dr. Leonard B. Welsh
Dr. Claire M. Welsh
Dr. J. Calvin Wenger
Dr. Allen C. Wesdorf
Dr. Thomas J. West
Dr. Christina E. West
Dr. Frederocl A. Weston
Dr. Gerald L. Whalen
Dr. Jacqueline M. Whalen
Dr. Jeffrey L. White
Dr. Ingrid E. White
Dr. Morris Whitehead
Dr. Mark Whitemyer
Dr. Cal B. Whitworth
Dr. David Wickes
Dr. Jonathan J. Widenbaum
Dr. James P. Widhelm
Dr. Larry F. Widmer
Dr. Mark P. Wiegand
Glenda Wiese
Dr. David Wikenheiser
Dr. Francis Wilamosky
Dr. Lyle S. Wilcox
Dr. Jeffrey M. Wilder
Dr. Martin Wiles
Dr. Terry L. Wiley

## BOOK PURCHASE
(Cont.)

Dr. Christine A. Wilke
Dr. Riddel J. William
Dr. Douglas E. Williams
Dr. Boyd Williams
Dr. Randall G. Williams
Dr. Holly A. Williams
Dr. Nell K. Williams
Dr. Dale F. Williams
Dr. Felix F. Williams
Dr. Wesley A. Williams
Dr. Sheila Williams
Dr. Robert J. Williams
Daniel Williams
Benjamin Williams
Dr. Darrellyn Williams
Dr. John G. Williams
Dr. Sidney E. Williams

Dr. Tracey L. Williamson
Dr. Jerry R. Willis
Dr. John C. Willis
Dr. Almer J. Willis
Dr. Lee Willis
Dr. Michael A. Willis
Dr. Daryl D. Wills
Dr. Rosemarie Wilson
Dr. Sydney S. Wilson
Dr. Bret A. Wilson
Dr. Howard K. Wilson
Dr. Joe H. Wilson
Dr. Roger W. Wilson
Dr. Michael B. Wilson
Dr. Carroll H. Winkler
Dr. Kerwin P. Winkler
Dr. Barry Winkler
Dr. Carol Winston
Dr. Douglas O. Winter

Dr. Shirley I. Winter
Dr. Joan Winters
Dr. Michael A. Winters
Dr. James F. Winterstein
Dr. R. Jay Wipf
Dr. Robert M. Wirthlin
Dr. Lawrence T. Withum
Dr. Evelyn M. Wofford
Dr. John J. Wohar
Dr. Gary L. Wojeski
Dr. Bryan R. Wolfe
Dr. Paul A. Wolfson
Dr. William H. Wolfsonidl
Dr. Richard E. Wollenberg
Dr. Timothy P. Wolter
Dr. Harrie E. Wolverton
Dr. Michael Wonder
Dr. Thomas A. Wong
Dr. John Wood

Dr. Charles W. Wood
Dr. Jeff Wood
Dr. Ronald W. Woods
Dr. Barbara Woolcott
Dr. Juliet R. Worley
Harold P. Wright
Dr. Kirk & Susan Wright
Dr. Ronald L. Wuest
Dr. Brian Wussow
Dr. Lawrence J. Wyatt, Jr
Dr. Shiro Yagishita
Dr. Robert L. Yakovac
Dr. Karen A. Yale
Dr. Shohei Yamagata
Dr. Yukio Yamamoto
Dr. Lee G. Yardley
Dr. Eva Yeomans
Dr. A. Scott Yerrick
Dr. Lester Yoos

Dr. James W. Young
Dr. Robert B. Young
Dr. Thersa M. Young
Dr. Kristofer P. Young
Dr. Ann-Marie Yvroux
Dr. Frank E. Zaccaria
Dr. Jonelle J. Zager
Dr. Brian W. Zaleski
Dr. Gwain R. Zarbuck
Dr. Henry G. Zastrow
Dr. Merlin R. Zelm
Dr. Mark A. Zelm
Dr. Alan E. Zelm
Dr. Clyde Zerba
Dr. Peter Zilahy
Dr. Jan Zinkernagel
Dr. Joe E. Zollinger
Dr. Randy R. Zolman
Dr. Thomas J. Zorich
Dr. Winsen C. Zouzal